What others are saying about this book:

"As alarming as it is educ...and. *Street Weapons*...ill open the eyes of the most exp...............n Vazquez, Training Commander, ...

"Reading *Street Weapons* ...ay gi....... ...fficer. ...he knowledge necessary to legal....... ...entify and ...ize ...al weapons. The book is an excellent resource for officers who work the streets." — Vance McLaughlin, Ph.D., Director of Training, Savannah, Georgia Police Dept.

"*Street Weapons* is, by far, the best manual on unusual weapons that I have seen in almost 25 years in law enforcement. It should be required reading for all cops, from rookies to veterans." — Officer Joseph Truncale, Glenview, IL Police Dept.

"*Street Weapons* offers professional insight into possible demonstrative evidence for police defense attorneys. Undoubtedly, its value will be significant in the legal defense of certain types of cases, and will also be significant for prosecutors, such as district attorneys, in the prosecution of criminal cases." — Attorney Mark T. Baganz, President, National Criminal Justice Research Institute.

"*Street Weapons* could not have come along at a better time. This text will go a long way towards enlightening our officers and, hopefully, will ultimately save many lives. Maybe we can't change our resources, but we can educate our officers." — Lt. Robert Wilson, Training Supervisor, Palm Beach County, FL Sheriff's Office.

"*Street Weapons* is must reading for any officer concerned with personal safety or survival - Read It Now!" — Officer Guy Rossi, Rochester, NY Police Dept.

"If you work the streets as a police officer, reading *Street Weapons* may save your life." — James Lindell, President, National Law Enforcement Training Center (NLETC).

"A giant step toward officer survival because it encompasses information that would take a career to experience. *Street Weapons* will change your mind-set about dangerous 'weapons' forever!" — Robert Bragg, Defensive Tactics Training Coordinator, Washington State Criminal Justice Training Commission.

Reading this book could keep you alive!!!

Dedication

This book is dedicated to the men and women who serve and protect our great nation. America's finest — the American Law Enforcement Officer!

"It isn't important to come out on top, what matters is to be the one who comes out alive."

— Bertolt Brecht

Street Weapons

An identification manual for improvised, unconventional, unusual, homemade, disguised, and exotic personal weapons.

by

Edward J. Nowicki

and

Dennis A. Ramsey

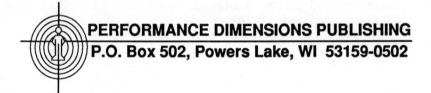

PERFORMANCE DIMENSIONS PUBLISHING
P.O. Box 502, Powers Lake, WI 53159-0502

Street Weapons

An identification manual for improvised, unconventional, unusual, homemade, disguised, and exotic personal weapons.

by
Edward J. Nowicki
and
Dennis A. Ramsey

Published by:

PERFORMANCE DIMENSIONS PUBLISHING
a division of Performance Dimensions, Inc.

P.O. Box 502, Powers Lake, WI 53159-0502, U.S.A.
Phone (414) 279-3850

Copyright © 1991 by Performance Dimension, Inc.
First Printing: January, 1991
Printed in the United States of America

Publisher's Cataloging in Publication

Nowicki, Edward J., 1947-
    Street weapons : an identification manual for improvised, unconventional, unusual, homemade, disguised, and exotic personal weapons / by Edward J. Nowicki and Dennis A. Ramsey. --
    p. cm.
    Includes bibliographical references.
    ISBN 1-879411-11-3 (pbk.)

    1. Arms and armor--Identification. 2. Knives--Identification. 3. Firearms--Identification. 4. Bombs--Identification. 5. Incendiary weapons--Identification. 6. Martial arts weapons--Identification. I. Ramsey, Dennis A. II. Title.

HV8077   623.44
                                              90-92207
                                              MARC

Library of Congress Catalog Card Number: 90-92207
ISBN: 1-879411-11-3: $19.95 Softcover

Table of Contents

Dedication   v
Epigraph   vii
Foreword by Massad Ayoob   xvii
Preface   xix
Acknowledgements   xxi
Introduction   xxv
Disclaimer   xxix

Section One: Edged and Pointed Weapons   1
   Ace of Spades   2
   Atchisson Folding Hunter   3
   Ballistic Knife   4
   Belt Buckle Knife - Knife Sheath in Belt   6
   Black Eagle   7
   Blow Gun   8
   Box Cutters   9
   Box Cutter Keychain   10
   Bracelet Knife   11
   Camper Saw   12
   Cat Claw Dagger   13
   Chain Pull Switchblade   14
   Chain Saw Whip   15
   Chinese Spinwheel   16
   Cigarette Lighter/Knife   17
   Cobra Kicker   18
   Cobra Pen Knife   19
   Comb Knife   20
   Concealable Flat Survival Tool   21
   Cutting Credit Card   22
   Cutting Garrote   23
   Defender   24
   Defender Belt Buckle Knife   25
   Delta Dart   27
   Double Bladed Dagger   28
   Executive Icepick   29
   Executive Ice Scraper   30

Executive Letter Opener   31
Folding Knuckle Knife   32
Fork Knuckles   33
Garden Rake Claw Weapon   34
Gerber Belt Buckle Knives   35
Guardfather   37
Guardian Ring   38
Hair Pick Weapon   39
Hat Pins   40
Hay Hook   41
Hideaway Ice Pick   42
Inner City Sportsman's Pencil   43
Key Fob with a Hidden Razor Blade   44
Key Knives   45
Knife in Necktie   46
Knife under Lapel   47
Knife Keychains   48
Knuckle Dagger/Push Dagger   49
Knuckle Knife   50
Knuckle Star   51
Kubotan Handle Keychain Knife   52
Kubotan Keychain Knife   53
Letter Opener/Push Dagger   54
Lip-Stick   55
Lollipop Knife   56
Mascara Needle   57
Money Clip Knife   58
Motorcycle Gas Cap Knife   59
Nail Knuckles   60
Nail Pen   61
Nail Polish Spike   62
Necklace Knives   63
Needle Pens   64
Ninja Claw   65
Ninja Knife Forearm Band   66
Ninja Needles   67
Ninja Needles Kubotan   68
Ninja Spiked Fist Band   69

Contents

Non-Traditional Opening Knives   70
Pen and Pencil Set Butterfly Knife   71
Pen Butterfly Knife   72
Pen Knives   73
Pocket Clip Folding Knife   74
Pop Open Knife on Lanyard   75
Push Dagger Buckle   76
Push Dagger in Wallet   78
Rattlesnake Bracelet Knife   79
Razor Knuckles   80
Ready Edge   81
Riding Crop Sword   82
Ruler/Letter Opener   83
Sharpened Keys   84
Sharpened Sunglasses   85
Shell Casing Knife   86
Shotgun Shell Knife   87
Sliding Blade Keychain   88
Spike Pods   89
Steel Porcupine   90
Stiletto Pen   91
Survival Tool Wallet   92
Switchblade Comb/Knife   94
Sword Canes   95
Sword Umbrella   96
Tekna Security Card   97
Three to Six Blade Throwing Star   98
Throwing Darts   99
Throwing Stars   100
Watch Cat   101
Whip Stabbing Device   102
World War I Trench Knife   103
Yawara Knife   104

Section Two: Firearms   105

Altered Handlebar Shotgun   106
Athletic Support Concealment   107
Baby Browning in Gun Wallet Holster   108

Belt Mounted Gun   109
Beretta Holster Gun Wallet   110
Billy Club Shotgun   111
Bolt Gun   112
Cane Gun   113
Car Door Shotgun   114
Double Barrelled Firearm   115
Dual-Purpose Cigarette Lighter   116
Equalizer Ring Gun   117
Electrical Connector Shotgun   118
Firing Jewelry   119
Hide-A-Gun   120
Highway Flare Shotgun   121
Jewelry Box with Gun Booby Trap   122
Keychain Gun   123
Knife Gun   124
Krupp K.K. Super Weapon   125
Leg Wallet Holster   126
Loaded Armrest   127
Magazine Shotgun   128
Mini-Revolvers   129
Mini-Revolver Buckle   130
Mini-Revolver in Cigarette Box   131
Mini-Revolver in Glove   132
Mini-Revolver in Hat   133
Mini-Revolver in Necktie   134
Mini-Revolver Holster/Grip   135
Mini-Revolver Pager Holsters   136
Pen Guns   137
Pipe Shotgun   138
Pouch with Hidden Gun Holster   140
Rat Trap Firearm   141
Shark Killer   142
Shirt Tail Holster   143
Shock Absorber Shotgun   144
Shotgun Shovel   145
Smoking Pipe Guns   146
Tire Iron Shotgun   147

Tire Pressure Gauge Gun   148

Section Three: Impact Weapons   149
Automatic Baton   150
Expandable Keychain   151
Expandable Straight Batons   152
Gunstick   153
Handler-12 and Sccpter Batons   154
Homemade Clubs   155
Key Defense Keychain   156
Knockout Cap   157
Knuckles   158
Knuckle Buckle   159
Ninja Shobo   160
Nunchaku   161
Nunchaku Baton   162
PR-24® Expandable Baton   163
Sap Gloves   164
Striking Keychains   165
Tonfa   166
T-Hold Yawara Stick   167
Yawara Stick   168
Yawara Style Keychains   169

Section Four: Explosives and Incendiaries   170
Aerosol Can Flame Thrower   171
Booby Trapped Shotgun   172
Bookshelf Device   173
Briefcase Device   174
Can with a Dual Detonation System   175
Cartridge Box Bomb   176
Cassette Player Device   177
Cement Hand Grenade   178
Cherry Bomb Grenade   179
Cigarette Pack Bomb   180
CO_2 Cylinder Explosive   181
Explosive Cigarette Lighter   182
Explosive Fountain Pen   183

Flashlight Explosive   184
Gas Tank Bomb   185
Impact Bomb   186
Letter Bomb   187
Mail Slot Incendiary   188
Mouse Trap Device   189
Package Bomb   190
Pen Device   191
Pipe Bombs   192
Pipe Bomb Impact Grenade   193
Refrigerator Bomb   194
Shotgun Shell Bomb - One Shell   195
Shotgun Shell Bomb - Multiple Shells   196
Shotgun Shell Bomb - Plunger Type   197
Spark Plug Explosive   198
Tennis Ball Device   199

Section Five: Miscellaneous Weapons   200

Chain Grip Come-A-Long   201
Cigarette Lighter Sprayer   202
Cigarette Sprayer   203
Electric Stun Guns   204
Fishing Hooks in Pant Seams   205
Iron Claw   206
Ju-Jo Magnum   207
Penalyzer   208
Pepsi Can Liquid Sprayer   209
Slingshot   210
Watch-It   211

Section Six: Concealed Carry Containers   212

Book Safe   213
Car Battery Safe   214
Coin and Pager Containers   215
Keychain Box   216
Magazine or Newspaper Carry Method   217
Product Safes   218

Section Seven: Of Special Interest to Law   219
                Enforcement
    Assorted Handcuff Keys   220
    Ball Point Pen Refill Handcuff Key   221
    Belt Buckle Back-Up   222
    Cross Handcuff/Leg Iron Key   223
    Guardian Attache   224
    Guardian Equipment Bag   226
    Guardian U.S.A. Bag   228
    Gunny Sack   230
    Handcuff Key Hidden on Belt Buckle   231
    Handcuff Key Keychain   232
    Hidden Agenda Bag   233

Afterword   **235**
Bibliography   **237**
Biography   **239**
Order Form   **241**

Foreword

Since the beginning of the Officer Survival movement, street cops have been cautioned about the ingenious hidden weapons criminals use to overpower them and avoid arrest. The inventiveness of the hardened criminal is limited only by his native animal cunning, which he tends to possess in considerable abundance.

Few men have the combined credibility as the authors of "Street Weapons" in this deadly arena. I first met Ed Nowicki and Dennis Ramsey through the Monadnock PR-24® baton training program, where we all serve as International Instructors, certifying those who will train other trainers in this life-saving instrument. Later, we all became charter members of ASLET, the American Society of Law Enforcement Trainers, which now includes thousands of those who mold America's police.

Ed began his career as a Chicago street cop and narc. Several gunfights and countless street brawls later, he became a chief of police, and finally a municipal judge before devoting himself full time to police training as a police training specialist with Milwaukee Area Technical College and Executive Director of ASLET. I can personally attest to the gruelling eighty or so hours a week he devotes to his brothers and sisters in law enforcement.

Dennis Ramsey is an investigator with the Illinois Department of Professional Regulation. The veteran detective is cross-trained to high levels of instructorship in several disciplines of the martial arts and defensive tactics (police unarmed combat), as well as multiple baton systems and the use of deadly force. I can tell you first hand that Dennis is a comforting presence to have at your side when a streetfight seems to be developing on a Tijuana sidewalk.

The integrity and dedication of these two police role models will shine through the pages of *Street Weapons*. It is the first book for each, but I'm sure it will be the last for neither.

Pay careful attention to *Street Weapons*. Reread it. Share it with the other Good Guys. I can tell you now that *Street Weapons* will be required reading for every police officer under my command.

Knowledge is power, and the history of human conflict proves that you have only a dim chance of defeating an enemy you don't understand. Knowing what to look for means a street weapon that is harmlessly confiscated instead of becoming Exhibit A in the death of a police officer.

The Good Guys can't beat the Bad Guys until they know what the Bad Guys are doing. This book will generate a great many arrests for illegal possession of street weapons that otherwise would have gone unnoticed. It will also, I am sure, keep an uncountable number of Good Guys off the casualty reports in the war on crime.

Don't just read *Street Weapons*, <u>study</u> it. The life it saves could be your own.

— Massad Ayoob
Concord, NH

Massad Ayoob has 16 years experience as a sworn police officer, from patrolman to captain, and is Director of Lethal Force Institute and the National Director of Police Firearms Training for ASLET.

Preface

This book is divided into seven sections in order to assist the reader in referencing different improvised, unconventional, homemade, disguised, and exotic personal weapons. These sections are as follows:

Section One: Edged and Pointed Weapons
The weapons in this section all have some type of edge or point that can stab, cut, and rip human flesh. Edged and pointed weapons can either be held in the hand, such as knives or ice pick type weapons, or propelled from the person, such as ninja knives or darts from blow guns.

Section Two: Firearms
Firearms included in this section are both homemade and commercially manufactured. Some look like conventional firearms, although they are quite small, while others look like something totally different. All of these weapons are legally classified as firearms.

Section Three: Impact Weapons
This section includes all weapons that are designed or used for striking another human being. Striking with a hand held weapon greatly intensifies any unarmed hand strike. These weapons include keychains, knuckles, and weighted gloves.

Section Four: Explosives and Incendiaries
The explosives in this section range from small explosive charges, which are actually modified commercial fireworks, to sophisticated hand held and very powerful explosives. Incendiaries primar-

ily produce fire rather than explosions.

Section Five: Miscellaneous Weapons

This section includes virtually any improvised, unconventional, homemade, disguised, and exotic personal weapons that are not classified under any of the four previously listed sections.

Section Six: Concealed Carry Containers

The containers in this section are frequently used to hide weapons or contraband (drugs, illegal items, etc.). Some, such as the car battery safe, are large, while others, such as the coin container, are small.

Section Seven: Of Special Interest to Law Enforcement

This section reveals to law enforcement officers some escape devices being used, such as modified handcuff keys. This section also includes some items that effectively allow plainclothes or off-duty law enforcement officers to remain covert while armed.

Acknowledgements

The authors would like to express their sincere gratitude to the many law enforcement officers and trainers who assisted them in their research over a four year time period. There are countless individuals who provided the authors with various weapons and expertise on the many dangers these weapons pose to law enforcement officers.

There are also many men and women who assisted, but chose to remain anonymous. Other individuals contributed, but inadvertently, neglected to provide their names.

We wish to thank the following individuals for their skill, wisdom, and advise which has assisted tremendously in the publishing of this manual:

Officer *Joseph J. Truncale*, Glenview, IL Police Dept.; Officer *Guy Rossi*, Rochester, NY Police Dept.; Lieutenant *Ernest Spiotto*, Chicago, IL Police Dept.; *Phil Messina*, President of Modern Warrior Defensive Tactics Institute, Lindenhurst, NY; Sergeant *John Vazquez*, Elizabeth, NJ Police Dept.; *Robert Lindsey*, Director of Security, Jefferson Parish, LA President's Office; *James Lindell*, Physical Training Supervisor, Kansas City, MO Regional Police Academy; Officer *Kevin Gordon*, Cahokia, IL Police Dept.; *Terry Smith*, Director of Training Standards, Monadnock PR-24® Training Council, Inc., Fitzwilliam, NH; Lieutenant *Bob Wilson*, Palm Beach County, FL Sheriff's Office; Chief *James L. Smith*, Randall, WI Police Dept.; Sergeant *Art Sapp*, Colorado Springs, CO Police Dept.; Officer *Steve Kaminski*, Cudahy, WI Police Dept.; *Mildred O'Linn*, Legal Advisor, Law Enforcement Television Network, Carrollton, TX; Constable *Robert Haas*, Town of Wheatland, WI Police Dept.; Lieutenant *Larry Smith* (retired), San Diego, CA Police Dept.; *Charles Remsberg* and *Dennis Anderson* of Calibre Press, Northbrook, IL;

Chief *Dale Crichton* and Sergeant *Wayne Trongeau,*
Twin Lakes, WI Police Dept.; Acting Director *Janet
M. Gunther,* Office of Intelligence, U.S. Customs
Service, Washington, DC; Inspector *Richard J.
Hoffman,* U.S. Marshals Service, Glynco, GA;
Sergeant *Harvey Hedden,* Kenosha County, WI
Sheriff's Office; Major *John Makholm,* Punta
Gorda, FL Police Dept.; Doctor *Mikel A. Rothberg,*
M.D., Walla Walla, WA; *Charles E. Humes, Jr.,*
Director of A.P.P.L.E. P.I.T.T., Toledo, OH; Officer
W. Denson, Shiner, TX Police Dept.; Detective *Paul
Casalese,* Ocean County, NJ Sheriff's Dept.; Judge
Jack Quinn, Boulder City, NV; *Mark Berggren,*
Marrero, LA; *Neal Trautman,* Director of Training,
Law Enforcement Television Network, Carrollton,
TX; *Vance McLaughlin,* Director of Training,
Savannah, GA Police Dept.; *Steve Bunting,*
Assistant Public Safety Director, University of
Delaware, Lewes, DE; *Paul Starrett,* President of
Monadnock Lifetime Products, Fitzwilliam, NH;
Sergeant *Terry Campbell,* Montgomery County, OH
Sheriff's Office; Attorney *Mark Baganz,* President
of NCJRI, Delafield, WI; *Bruce Siddle,* Director of
PPCT Management Systems, Waterloo, IL; Training
Officer *John Martin,* Ohio Peace Officers' Training
Academy, London, OH; Officer *Eric Nowicki,*
Genoa City, WI Police Dept.; *Roland Ouellette,*
President of R.E.B. Security Training, Avon, CT;
Deputy Marshall *Robert Musgrave,* Zionsville, IN
Police Dept.; *Rich Davis,* President of Second
Chance Body Armor, Inc., Central Lake, MI; Officer
Robert Littlejohn, Bellevue, WA Police Dept.; *H.J.
"Jim" Beach,* Union Pacific Railroad Police, Omaha,
NE; *Steve Cohen* and *Jack H. Lewis,* Hidden
Agenda, Seattle, WA; *Bob Smith,* Guardian Leather,
Newton Center, MA; *Marlene Chicco,* American
Security Training Institute, Chicago, IL; *Thomas
Owen* and *Mitch Shore,* Shore Galleries, Inc.,
Lincolnwood, IL; *Mike Jones* and *Keith Mandic,*
Ray O'Herron Company, Oak Brook Terrace, IL;
John Amado, The Thin Blue Line, Wood Dale, IL;

Acknowledgements xxiii

David J. Walczak, Continental Security, Maywood, IL; *Steve Horwitz,* Buffalo Grove, IL; *Ted Leverenz,* Illinois State Representative of Maywood, IL; Officer *Patrick Martin,* George Washington University Police Dept., DC; *Anthony Gregory* and *George Voltz,* Tactical Training Associates, Indianapolis, IN; *Massad Ayoob,* Director, Lethal Force Institute, Concord, NH; Officer *Dennis Jurasz,* North Tonawanda, NY Police Dept.; Officer *Mary Gifford,* Purdue, IN University Police Dept.; *Brian Yerich,* President, S.E.T.D., Inc., Stamford, NY; *Bill Berry,* Vice President, L.E. Net, Chesterfield, MO; *Judy Leventhal,* Video Producer, St. Louis, MO; Special Agent *Ron Feurer,* Wisconsin Division of Criminal Investigation; *Doug Hinkle,* President, Observation Skills Institute, VA. Officer *David H. Steven,* Rosemont, IL Department of Public Safety; and Officer *Dennis Cerqua,* Schaumburg, IL Police Department.

Introduction

Since the first caveman picked up the first club, man began to realize the advantages of weapons. The first clubs evolved into sharpened sticks, and the sharpened sticks evolved into finely honed metal knives and spears. Weapons can be used for either good or evil in the hands of man, but weapons themselves are neither good nor evil, since they are only inanimate objects. It is man that determines how and when a weapon is used.

Remember that the first terrorist was a caveman who picked up a rock or club to influence the behavior of the first victim. It is a tremendous leap from a broken branch to a sharpened stabbing instrument. Turning a simple branch into a sharpened stabbing instrument required a certain amount of planning and execution. After all, monkeys can – and do – pitch coconuts, stones, and sticks. However, and this is what separates man from other creatures, it requires human intelligence to perceive (a) the need for a given instrument, (b) the raw material from which to fashion the instrument, and (c) the process by which the gap between raw material and finished product can be closed. It then requires both memory and patience to sustain the effort between idea and achievement.

Back to the sharpened stick. At some point someone discovered that certain types of wood, when held in flame, became much harder. Bamboo is a good example. Its ability to pierce without losing its point is greatly increased when heated. Hence, fire-hardened spears are still in use today among certain aboriginal tribes.

Here the thinking process took another big step. Someone noticed a cause-and-effect relationship in one area (annealing) and applied it to something entirely different (combat/hunting). This required a combination of observation repeated over an extended period – reasoning, experimentation, and industry sustained by patience and imagination – a complicated process indeed.

That same four-step process, observation, reasoning, experimentation, and industry, led to the development and refinement of hunting (and perhaps simultaneously to armed combat) as an art form. Consider these successive stages:
- Fire-hardened pointed sticks
- Sticks with tips of chipped flint (arrows)
- Bows to propel the sticks
- Sticks with tips of metal
- Bows with shoulder-stocks (crossbows)
- Shoulder-stocks with metal barrels utilizing explosive chemicals to propel lead balls (rifles).

Each stage required an investment of ingenuity, time, and industry that we can only appreciate by imagining ourselves in an earlier time with a need for more sophisticated weaponry.

It is not our purpose here to offer a history of such weaponry. That has already been done. Nor do we presume to examine the psychological processes necessary in devising weapons. We are law enforcement officers, not psychologists. We do, however, wish to make the following points:

(1) When you feel a desire to physically overcome someone for whatever motive – self-defense, criminal assault, robbery – you can either do it with your bare hands, or you can do what people have done since the caveman — use a weapon.

(2) If you have plenty of time, you can think the weapon out carefully and refine it. Depending on your criminal intent and your motivation to inflict pain or injury, you can be quite inventive.

(3) In the absence of conventional weapons (guns, clubs, commercial knives), your motivation may be very strong. Regrettably, the streets are full of criminals who fall into this category. Their state of mind is probably not very different from that of pre-historic man. Some of them take an apparent diabolical pleasure in devising variations of weapons

that are intended to disfigure, maim, or kill.

(4) These are the people that law enforcement officers must face as a matter of routine.

The descriptions, photos, and drawings included in this book have been described as unusual, improvised, disguised, unconventional, exotic, and hidden. It is much easier to classify all these weapons simply as "Street Weapons." These various "Street Weapons" are both commercially manufactured and homemade.

Law enforcement officers must realize that "Street Weapons" are on our nation's streets, and that these weapons are instruments of death. Officers should be extremely cautious when observing any item on or about a person's body. A relatively harmless looking pen may actually be a knife, or even a gun. An ornate belt buckle may hide a knife, while even a comb may produce an ice pick type pointed weapon.

This manual is by no means complete. Newly manufactured and modified "Street Weapons" are constantly being carried and used. A pencil wound to the heart has been documented as fatal. A rolled-up newspaper can deliver lethal strikes, and a common teaspoon can easily gouge an eyeball from its socket.

The weapons shown and described in this book are not intended to make officers paranoid. This manual was written to inform our nation's law enforcement officers of the many potential threats. When dealing with various individuals, officers must learn to ask themselves, "What if this is a weapon" and "How could it be used against me" in their observations.

The videotape companion to this manual, *Street Weapons – The Video*, should be viewed by officers so they become familiar on how various "Street Weapons" can be used. This twenty minute video, professionally produced in cooperation with L.E. Net, graphically recreates various officer-suspect contacts and provides explanations and demonstrations of numerous "Street Weapons."

Readers are encouraged to contact the authors, in care of the publisher, if they have any information on any other "Street Weapons," and how they were carried and/or used. The authors also request black and white photos of new "Street Weapons" or, if possible, the actual weapons. Please read the "Afterword" at the end of this book for complete details.

Our nation's law enforcement officers must stay informed, alert, well trained, and more important, alive. Hopefully, this manual and accompanying videotape will help in this endeavor.

– Edward J. Nowicki
– Dennis A. Ramsey

Warning–Disclaimer

This book is designed to provide information in regard to the subject matter covered. It is sold with the understanding that the publisher and authors are not engaged in rendering legal or other professional services. If legal or other professional assistance is required, the services of a competent professional should be sought.

It is not the purpose of this manual to reprint all the information that is otherwise available to the authors and/or publisher, but to complement, amplify and supplement other texts. You are urged to read all the available material, learn as much as possible about weapon identification, officer safety and survival and to tailor the information to your individual needs. For more information, see the "Bibliography" at the end of this book.

Every effort has been made to make this manual as complete and as accurate as possible. However, there may be mistakes, both typographical and in content. Therefore, this text should be used only as a general guide and not as the ultimate source of identification of all "Street Weapons." Furthermore, this manual contains information on "Street Weapon" identification only up to the printing date.

The purpose of this manual is to educate, inform, and stimulate thought. The authors and Performance Dimensions shall have neither liability nor responsibility to any person or entity with respect to any loss or damage caused, or alleged to be caused, directly or indirectly by the information contained in this book.

If you do not wish to be bound by the above, you may return this book to the publisher for a full refund.

Section One:

Edged and Pointed Weapons

"The arrow seen before cometh less rudely"

— Dante

The weapons listed in this section all have some type of edge or point. They can all stab, cut, puncture, or rip human flesh. These edged and pointed weapons can either be held in the hand, or carried on the person, such as throwing knives or darts from blow guns. Many models of soft body armor will stop a bullet fired from a firearm, but the vest may not be able to stop the penetration of a very pointed weapon. Caution is always advised.

Ace of Spades

A push dagger made of high impact hardened plastic with a two inch blade that can be made extremely sharp. This weapon cannot be detected by the metal detectors used for court and airport security.

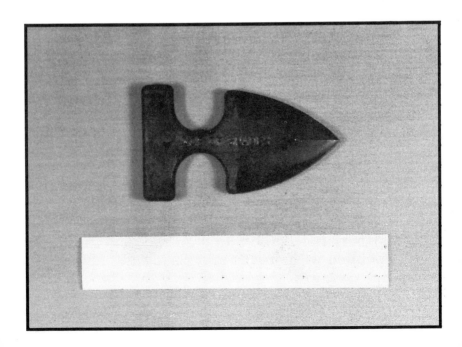

Atchisson Folding Hunter

A commercially manufactured weapon made of high quality, tough carbon steel hardened and heat treated with a black oxide finish. This four bladed knife folds and opens easily. Weighing in at one pound, this weapon is 6 5/8 inches long and opens to 12 inches. When properly thrown, this weapon can penetrate 3/4 inch plywood at 20 yards.

Ballistic Knife

Also known as the "KGB Ballistic Knife," and looks like an ordinary dagger when held in the hand. The knife's blade is propelled from the handle by a compressed spring and firing mechanism. The 4 1/2 inch blade can be propelled up to 30 feet and penetrates many models of soft body armor. The knife's hard metal sheath can also be fired as a blunt object and delivers a powerful blow.

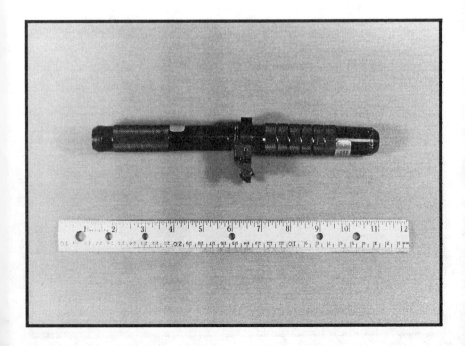

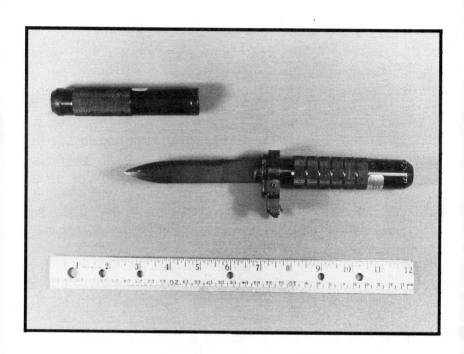

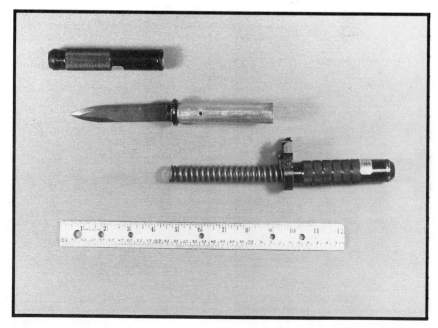

Belt Buckle Knife - Knife Sheath in Belt

Available in a variety of shapes, sizes, and styles. This double-edged or single-edged blade is normally 2 to 3 inches long. Usually this knife is slightly curved to fit into the belt, which serves as a sheath for the knife's blade. There is a metal stud located on the knife's shank, between the buckle and the blade, which fits into a hole on the belt. The stud is one key that helps identify this weapon, and also there is no buckle tongue on the buckle. This stud system usually leaves two holes visible between the leading edge of the buckle and the stud. This attractive belt and buckle appears very similar to most others, except for the stud fastening.

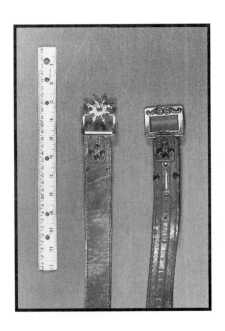
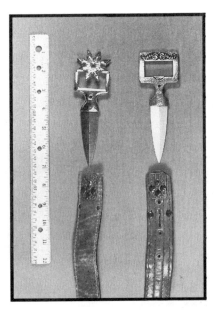

Black Eagle

A fixed blade knife that opens in a manner similar to the way a front opening stiletto knife opens. The "Black Eagle" has a 3 1/4 inch blade that is concealed behind a hard covering that serves as a sheath. When the spring-action button on the knife's handle is moved to the rear, the sheath moves to the rear and exposes the blade. The knife is closed by moving the spring-action button forward. Depending on how the laws are written in each state, this knife may be legal to possess in states where traditional switchblades are illegal.

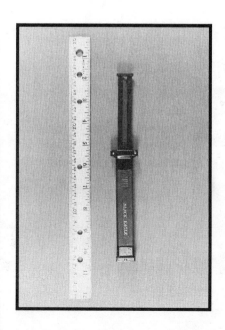
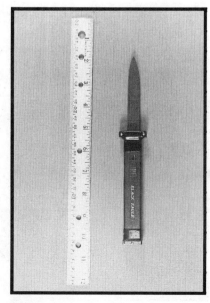

Blow Gun

A weapon that can fire various size darts powered by human breath. The harder the blow, the more velocity. The pointed metal tipped darts can easily penetrate exposed flesh. The darts can also be dipped in a poisonous substance to increase their effectiveness.

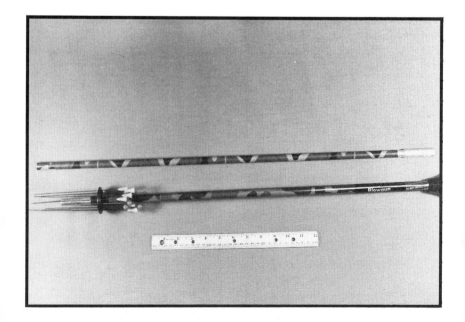

Box Cutters

Everyday box cutters can be deadly weapons when the cutting edges are exposed. Box cutters come in various sizes and shapes, and can be quickly opened to expose a sharp, but small, cutting blade.

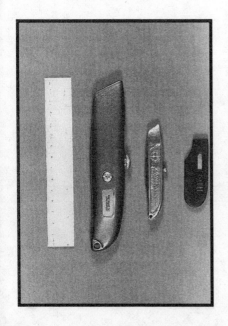
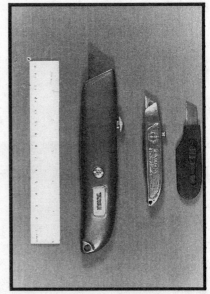

Box Cutter Keychain

A small harmless looking, but potentially lethal, keychain frequently sold near the check-out counters of many major food stores. The 5/8 inch blade is exposed by sliding the thumb button forward. The blade is withdrawn by sliding the thumb button backward.

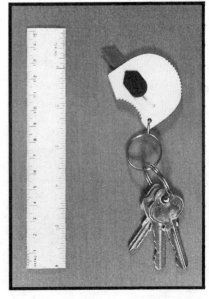

Bracelet Knife

A common type of bracelet knife is a smooth round plastic band that can be virtually any color. The clasp is actually a small knife that fits into the other end of the bracelet and serves as a sheath for the knife when closed. These bracelets appear to be rather cheaply made and harmless, but they can be deadly.

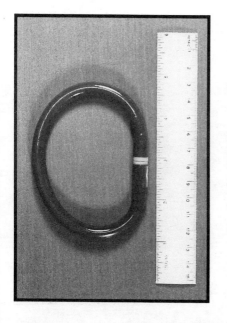
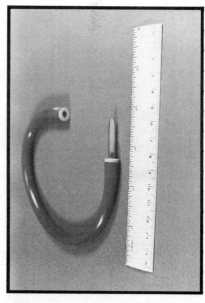

Camper Saw

A small and easily concealed camper saw features a fine, yet sharp and strong flexible saw blade fastened to a metal ring on each end. The rings fit over the fingers or thumbs and can be used in a fashion similar to the "Cutting Garrote." The saw can be carried coiled and easily hidden inside the waistband.

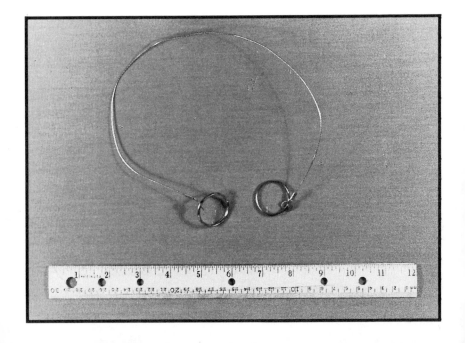

Cat Claw Dagger

Worn as a pendant on a chain, the "Cat Claw" actually conceals a push dagger with a double-edged blade. The pendant is about 3 1/2 inches long with a blade and shank length of about 2 1/2 inches. The pendant serves as the knife's sheath. The blade can be quickly removed by grabbing the handle and pulling the blade from the pendant.

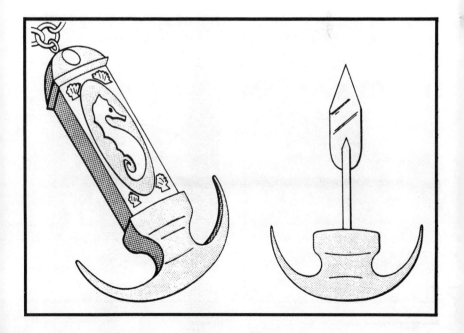

Chain Pull Switchblade

A switchblade knife frequently carried by many members of outlaw type motorcycle gangs. A chain is attached to a hole in the metal opening device at the end of the knife and when the chain is pulled tight, the opening device allows the knife to snap open in a fashion similar to the conventional switchblade knife. When opened, the 3 1/2 inch knife blade is locked open.

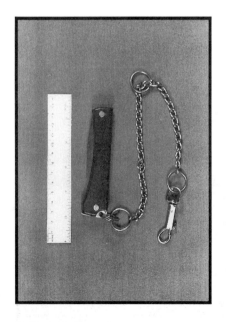
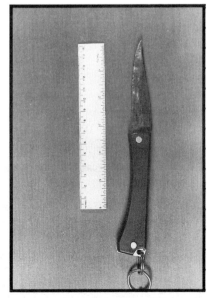

Chain Saw Whip

An extremely effective lacerating device. Constructed by nailing the end of a chain saw bladed chain to the end of a two to three foot long thick piece of wood, dowel, or baseball bat which serves as the handle. The wood handle is held in the hand and the chain is swung at the person. According to emergency medical personnel, the effects can be very serious.

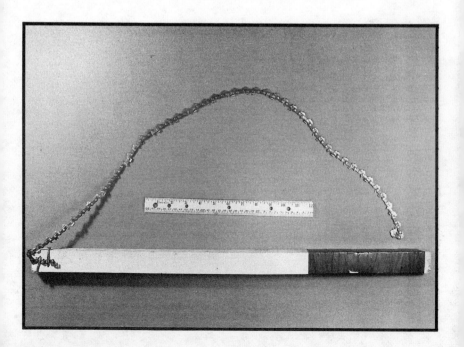

Chinese Spinwheel

A homemade weapon consisting of eight three and one-half inch length nails welded together to form a pronged device. When thrown, this device can strike an intended target with one or more of the nails, and if thrown hard enough, deeply puncture the body.

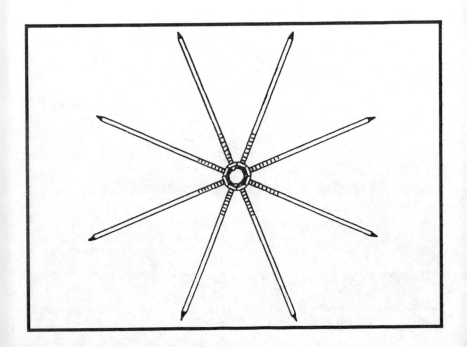

Cigarette Lighter/Knife

A rigid plastic holder molded to snugly hold a Bic cigarette lighter, while also containing a knife with a two inch blade. The blade is exposed by placing the thumb on a button on the back of the lighter and sliding the thumb forward. Once the thumb is removed, the blade is firmly ""locked" open. It is very difficult to distinguish this device from an ordinary Bic cigarette lighter.

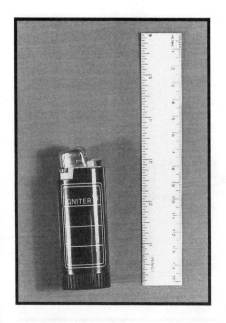
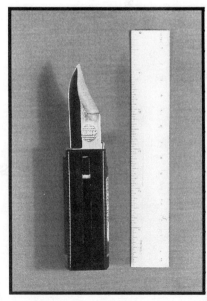

Cobra Kicker

A metal device worn between the laces of a shoe, and according to some advertising, worn for protection against rapists, muggers and dogs. The "Cobra Kicker" has a metal four-sided pointed shaft meant to pierce the flesh of the person being kicked. The target for the kick is supposed to be the groin area.

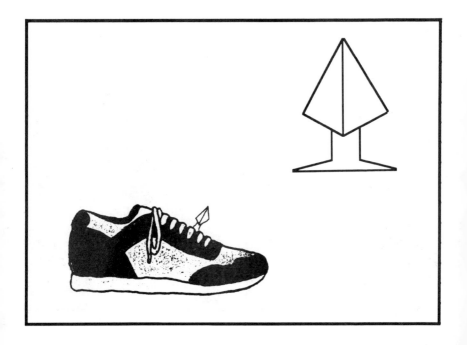

Cobra Pen Knife

A pen knife that provides the wearer with two options. A double threaded screw-in standard knife blade or a serrated blade can be made available by removing the pen's cap. This reversible blade option produces a blade of about 1 1/2 inches in length.

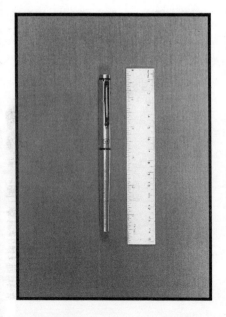
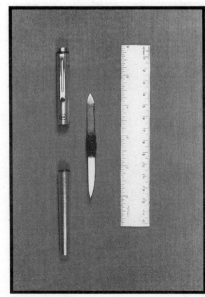

Comb Knife

A weapon that appears to be a metallic comb contained within a leather or black nylon case. Removing the "comb" from the case will expose a double-edged knife blade approximately 3 inches long.

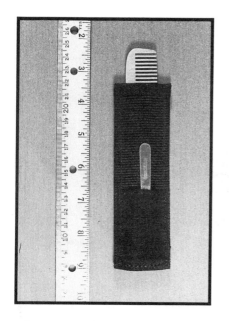 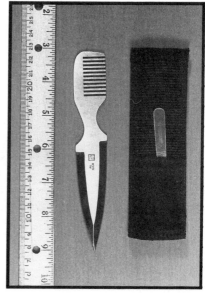

Concealable Flat Survival Tool

A small flat metal survival tool that easily mounts on the back of a credit card or drivers license. The tool can be taped to the back of a credit card or drivers license so that it can hinge outward and be held effectively between the index and middle finger for slashing. The extremely sharp cutting edge is approximately 1 1/2 inches in length.

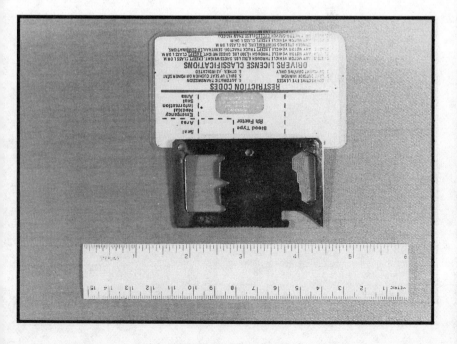

Cutting Credit Card

An ordinary plastic credit card, plastic coated driver's license, or any other plastic card can be used to easily conceal a single-edged razor blade on the back. Another dimension to this threat can be added by grinding down one or more sides of the credit card which produces a very sharp edge.

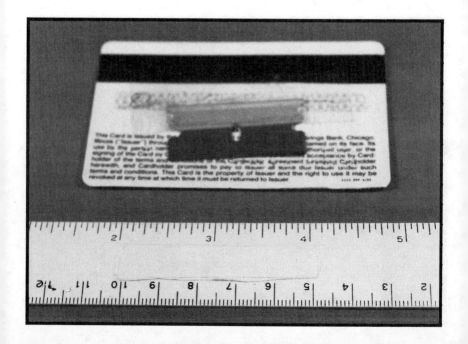

Cutting Garrote

A weapon that is fitted with an extremely fine, yet strong metal wire. The wire is actually very sharp, and can strangle and sever when used in the traditional garrote fashion around the neck. This weapon can also be used to sever or cut flesh on any other appendage.

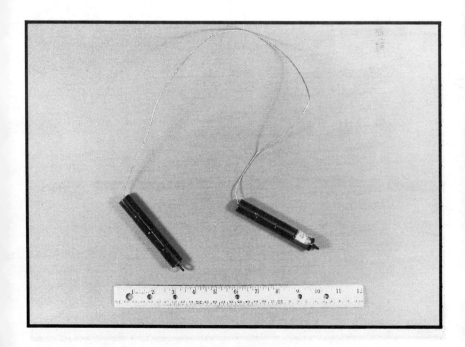

Defender

A weapon that looks like an ordinary comb, but by depressing a gravity operated release button, it releases a four inch, thin steel spike that remains locked until the release button is depressed again.

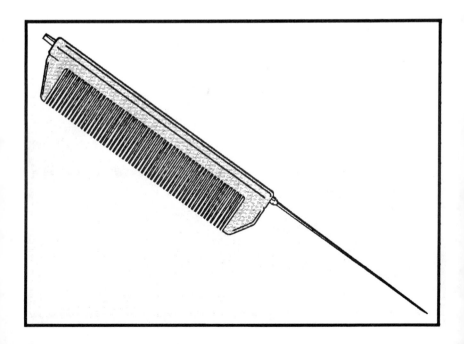

Defender Belt Buckle Knife

A belt buckle with a black plastic serrated edge and a smooth silver colored middle. The middle is suitable for initial engraving or as a surface for gluing small ornamentation, such as a large silver dollar. The buckle serves as the sheath for two extremely sharp edged metal weapons: one a small double-edged push dagger and the other a small slicing weapon. Part of the serrated plastic buckle border separates from the buckle to deploy either of these weapons.

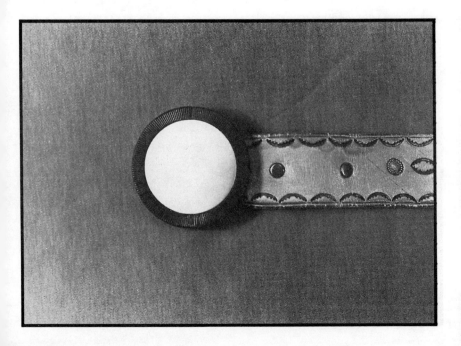

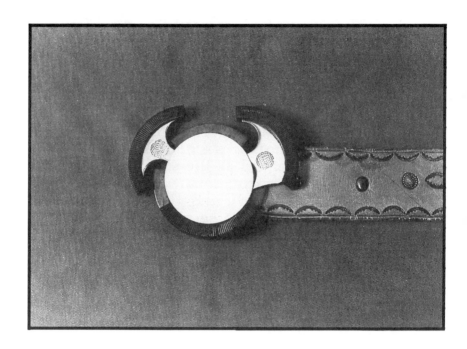

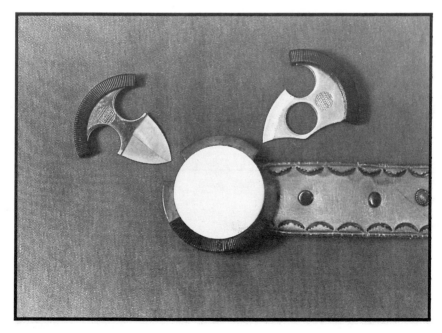

Delta Dart

A device with a triangular blade that has three edges, in addition to the point. The edges can be sharpened for cutting purposes, and the point has the ability to penetrate most soft body armor. "Delta Darts" can be made of hardened plastic and undetectable by metal detectors, or of metal. Although the metal "darts" can be thrown, they are primarily designed to be used as hand held weapons.

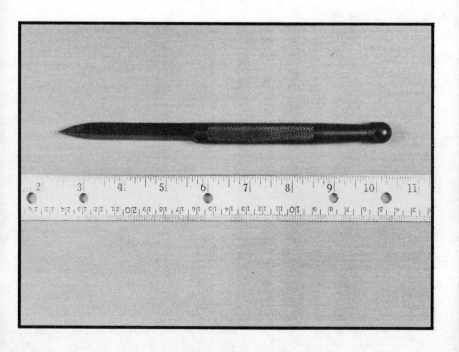

Double Bladed Dagger

An all metal knife that looks like an ordinary dagger and typically carried in a black nylon sheath. This double-edged 5 inch bladed dagger, however, has an unusual twist. It has a screw device located on the bottom of the handle. This device which extends a single-edged 2 inch blade knife, can be easily unscrewed in a covert fashion with the little finger of the hand holding the knife. The second blade is drawn back into the handle by screwing the device in the opposite direction.

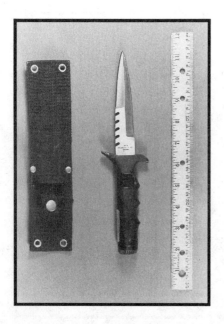 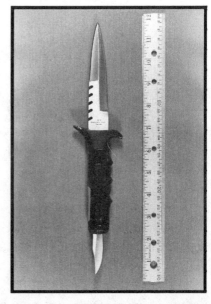

Executive Icepick

A distinguished looking pen, available in either black or chrome, which contains a hardened, sharpened steel rod exposed by removing the pen's cap. This steel rod can penetrate most soft body armor.

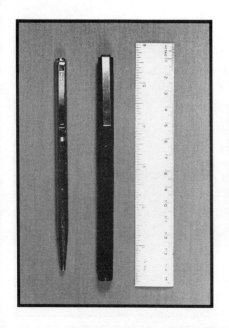
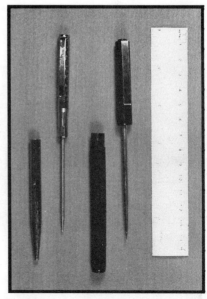

Executive Ice Scraper

An "ice scraper" with a two inch scraper blade that can legitimately be used to scrape car windows. Keys can be attached to the hole in the middle of the handle. Made of hardened plastic, this device is undetectable by metal detectors. A recent ad for this device advised, "CAUTION: Under no circumstances should you strike someone with your ice scraper as this will cause a particularly nasty cut requiring about 20 stitches to close."

Executive Letter Opener

Marketed as a letter opener since, according to an advertisement, "We still don't know of any laws that prevent the carrying of a plastic letter opener." This device, also known as "The Stinger," is made of super tough plastic and can be driven through 3/4 inch plywood with a hammer. A few different styles are available, most with blades three to four inches long. This device will go undetected through metal detectors.

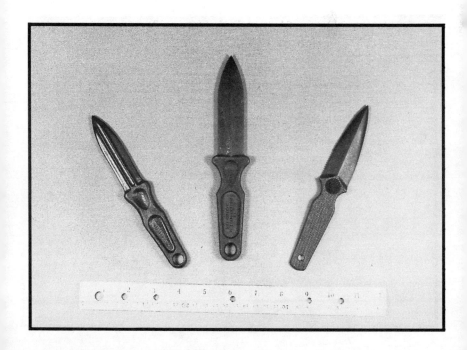

Folding Knuckle Knife

A device that can only be used effectively with the knife open, since it is impossible to fit any fingers in the knuckle holes when the knife is closed. This all black metal knife, with a blade approximately 3 inches long, is used in a similar fashion to the "World War I Trench Knife."

Fork Knuckles

An ordinary fork is shaped into a set of punching knuckles that can be used to rip and tear flesh. The fork can be easily molded to an individual's knuckles for a comfortable fit. The prongs, which are usually bent outward, provide for about 1/2 inch of penetration. The prongs can also be sharpened for an even greater effect.

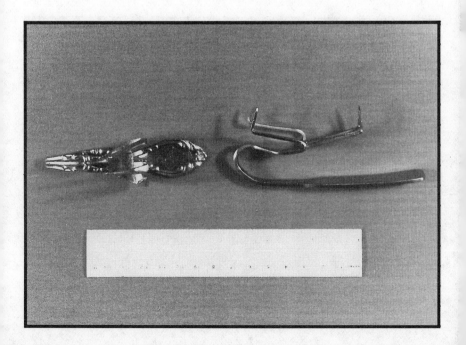

Garden Rake Claw Weapon

An ordinary three pronged garden rake can be made into an extremely effective clawing device by removing the rake's handle. This modified rake fits comfortably in the hand and can easily puncture and rip flesh. The rake's 1 inch prongs can also be sharpened to increase its effectiveness.

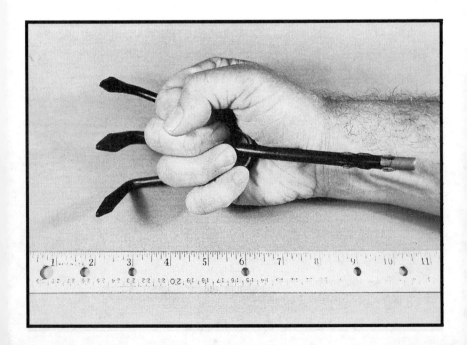

Gerber Belt Buckle Knives

A closed folding knife is actually the visible part of the belt buckle. This knife has two basic styles: one style's knife is positioned diagonally on a large buckle, while the other's knife is positioned horizontally on a smaller and dressier buckle. The knife is opened simply and quickly by moving the knife's handle down, exposing the blade and allowing the knife to be easily removed from the buckle.

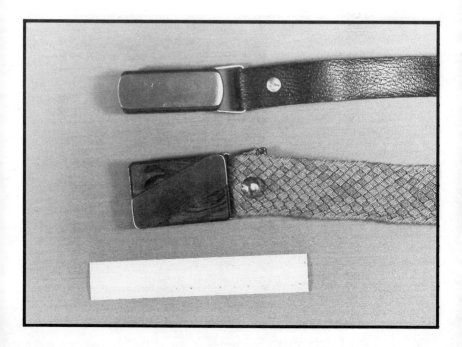

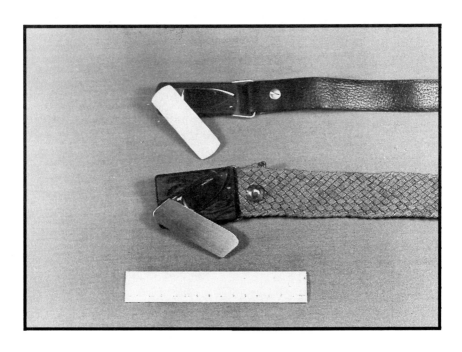

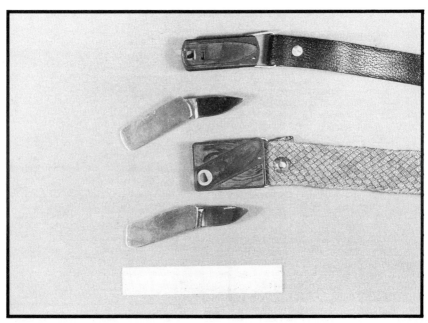

Guardfather

A blued finish, all metal device that looks almost like an ordinary pen when in a shirt pocket. A push of the pocket clip activates a spring fired device that projects a four-inch, hardened steel, tapered and pointed shaft in, according to the manufacturer, "...only 1/250th of a second." Tests conducted by the authors reveal that this weapon can penetrate most soft body armor.

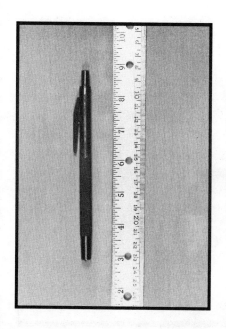
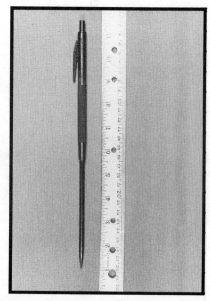

Guardian Ring

A ring that is worn on the finger that has two sharp and pointed 3/8 inch prongs exposed by placing pressure with the thumb on the side of the ring. When the prongs are open in the upright position, they can cut and tear flesh.

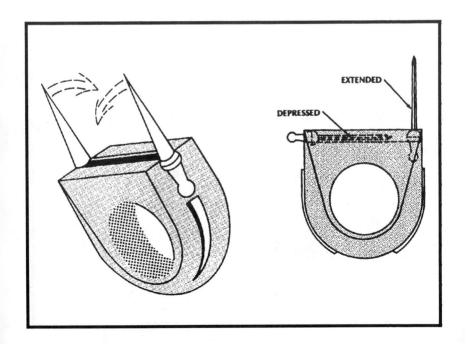

Hair Pick Weapon

A commercially manufactured hair pick normally used to comb Afro style hairdos. The picking part of the hair pick is made of metal with extremely sharp points. It can be held in the hand in a brass knuckle fashion, and easily lacerates human flesh if firm punches are used.

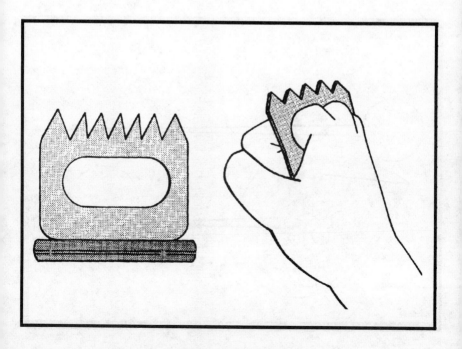

Hat Pins

A lady's conventional hat pin can be an extremely effective and potentially lethal weapon. Hat pins vary in length, but all are relatively difficult to find during a search, particularly when "pinned" in a garment's seam, or in any location where the cloth is relatively thick.

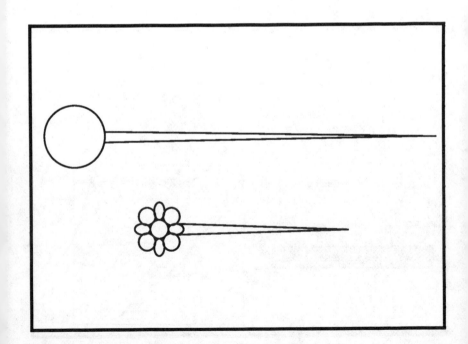

Hay Hook

A hook that is normally used on farms for moving bales of hay, or by dock workers for moving cargo. Frequently found concealed on a vehicle dashboard. The metal hook portion is placed through a hole in the dash, which only leaves the wooden handle exposed. A sharp pointed hook can deeply puncture and easily tear human flesh.

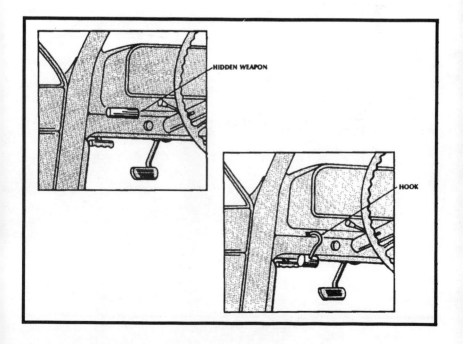

Hideaway Ice Pick

A commercially manufactured wooden weapon designed to be used as a martial arts "Yawara" stick for striking purposes. This weapon separates to reveal an ice pick type pointed shaft.

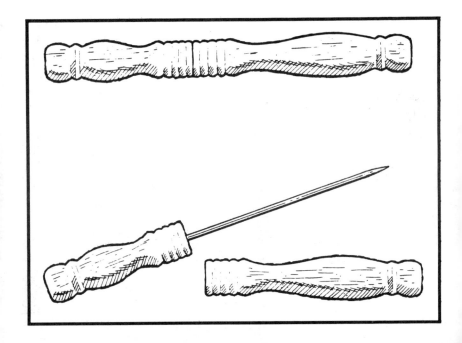

Inner City Sportsman's Pencil

A highly concealable, disguised stabbing instrument patterned after the "lancet" used by the the United States Office of Strategic Services (OSS). Two models of this device are available. One features a spring loaded steel spike in a draftsman's type mechanical pencil, while the other model has a gravity fed spike. This six inch pencil produces a 3 1/2 inch long spike.

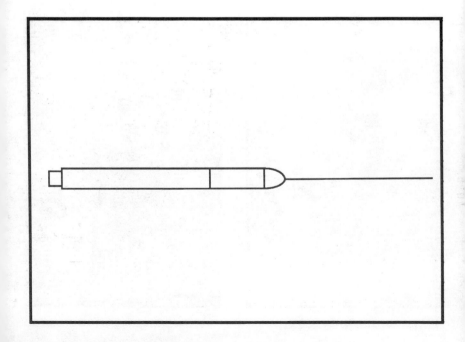

Key Fob with a
Hidden Razor Blade

An ordinary leather key fob can be slit in the seam on one end, and easily conceal a single edge razor blade between the outside and inside pieces of leather.

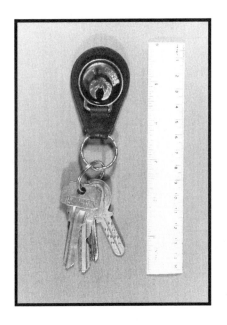

Key Knives

The "folding key knife" looks like an ordinary metal key, but closer inspection reveals a folding knife blade in the the teeth area of the key. This knife blade is approximately 2 1/2 inches long.

The plastic "razor key knife" is frequently used for advertising purposes with the name of a company printed on the key. Inside this key is a sharp razor type blade, approximately 5/8 inches long. The blade is exposed from the end of the key by sliding a button forward with the thumb.

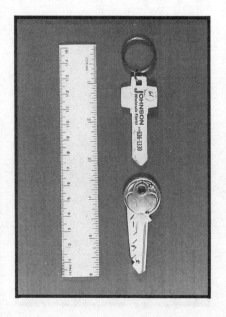

Knife in Necktie

A traditional necktie can be modified to discreetly conceal a large, but light weight and sharp, plastic dagger. A piece of velcro is taped to the flat dagger handle and the inside of the tie. The knife is inserted, point up, in the tie and held securely with the velcro. The bottom of the tie can be pulled up in order to expose the knife's handle for quick deployment.

 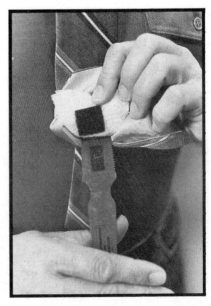

Knife under Lapel

A small fixed or folding blade knife can be adequately concealed under the lapel of a sports coat by affixing one end of a piece of wire to the end of the knife, and the other end of the wire onto an alligator clip. The alligator clip is then clipped to a piece of fabric under the lapel. The knife can be easily accessed when concealed in this manner.

Knife Keychains

Keychains that are, according to some advertising, designed to "get the edge in a rough situation." Tekna manufactures a keychain called "Xtra Edge," which is made of high impact plastic with a 1 1/2 inch stainless steel blade. This knife does not look like a knife to the untrained eye. Other keychain knives are usually about the same size, but are easier to identify as a knife.

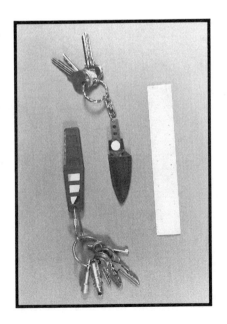

Knuckle Dagger/Push Dagger

A dagger featuring a black metal knuckle guard and carried in a traditional leather sheath. A blade locking mechanism is located at the back of the dagger which, when depressed, permits the blade to fold downward and "lock" for use as a punching push dagger. The 5 inch blade's shank allows the index finger to fit comfortably in the knuckle guard.

Knuckle Knife

A knife made of 1/8 inch thick stainless steel with a ring in the middle to slip over the middle finger. The ring and index finger fit into finger slots next to the middle ring which allows this weapon to be used in a fashion similar to brass knuckles. This small, flat device is easily concealed on the body.

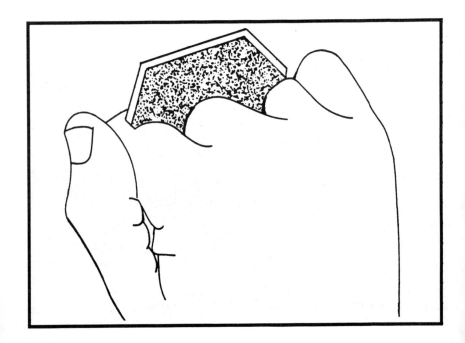

Knuckle Star

A weapon that is an enlarged and modified version of a throwing star, which can be held in the hand in a "brass knuckle" type fashion for punch type stabs, or used for throwing. This black metal weapon features five pointed blades which may, or may not, be sharpened.

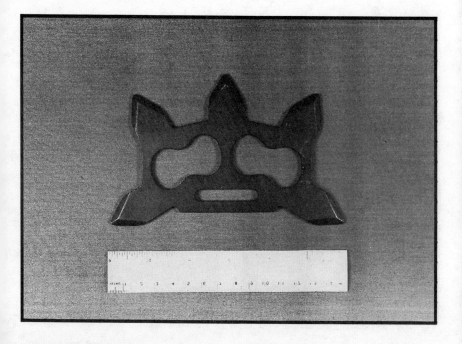

Kubotan Handle Keychain Knife

The threaded end of this keychain can be unscrewed to expose a hidden knife. The exposed knife blade is screwed into the open end of the kubotan, which serves as the knife's handle. The blade on this knife is approximately 2 1/2 inches in length.

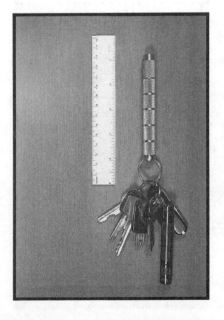 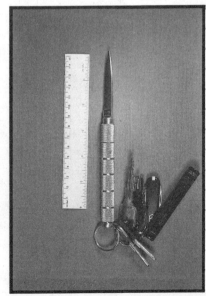

Kubotan Keychain Knife

A self-defense keychain that appears to be a standard Kubotan, but this model actually screws apart in the middle and exposes a metal knife blade of approximately 1 1/2 inches long. This type of weapon is available in various lengths. The longer models may be called a "Yawara Knife" or an "Urban Billy."

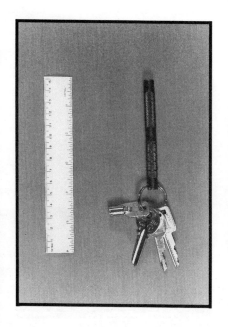
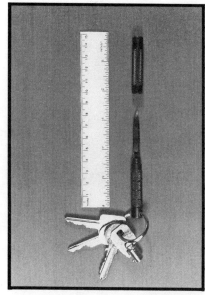

Letter Opener/Push Dagger

Frequently advertised as a "letter opener," this dagger type weapon has a locking mechanism that, when depressed, allows the 3 inch blade to "lock" in position for use as a push dagger. The knife blade's steel shank prevents the fingers from being cut when firmly held in the hand.

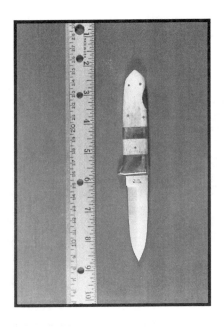

Lip-Stick

A weapon that looks like an ordinary tube of lipstick, except it is not found in the make-up bag of most ladies. When the end of the tube is twisted like an ordinary tube of lipstick, a knife blade is slowly extended. The knife's blade, when fully extended, is 1 1/2 inches in length.

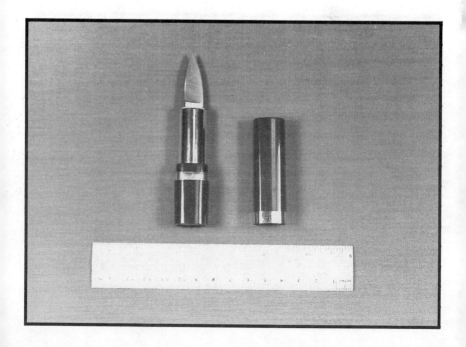

Lollipop Knife

A caramel colored disk, 1 1/2 inches in diameter and 1/2 inch thick, that looks like a piece of candy. The disk that serves as the handle, is secured to a round spike, which is a 3 1/2 inch long steel blade. A white plastic tube that looks like a lollipop stick fits over the blade to serve as a sheath.

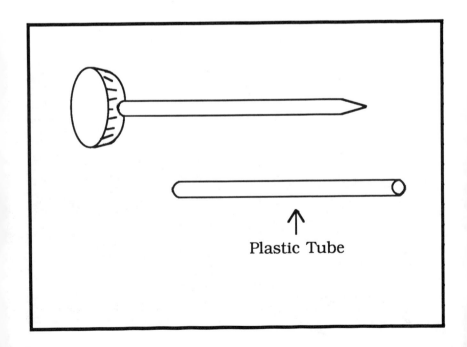

Plastic Tube

Mascara Needle

A standard tube of mascara is modified to contain a 1/2 inch long needle. It is necessary to closely inspect this item to discover the hidden weapon.

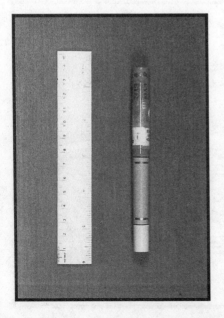 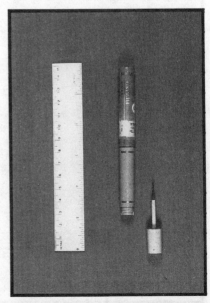

Money Clip Knife

The exposed side of this money clip looks like an ordinary money clip. However, a steel blade is located on the other side. The blade is concealed by sliding the blade between folded currency. They are either commercially available, or home made. The blade is usually 2 to 3 inches long.

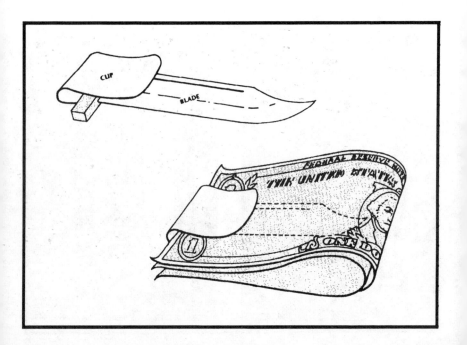

Motorcycle Gas Cap Knife

A knife blade is welded or brazed to the cap of an ordinary and fully functional motorcycle gas cap. In addition to covering the gas tank, the motorcycle cap discreetly hides a knife blade for quick access. These knife blades can be several inches long.

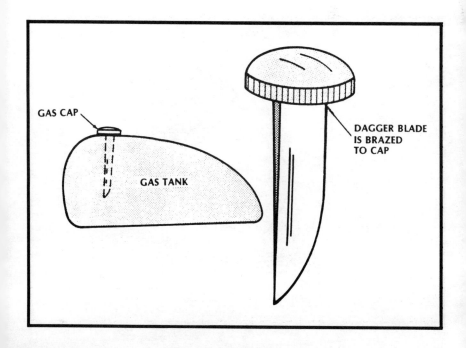

Nail Knuckles

A homemade weapon usually made of heavy tape with 15 to 20 uniform length nails (2 1/2 to 3 1/2 inches in length) embedded into the tape and protruding outward 1/4 to 1 inch. It is worn similarly to brass knuckles, and sharpening the points of the nails increases its effect.

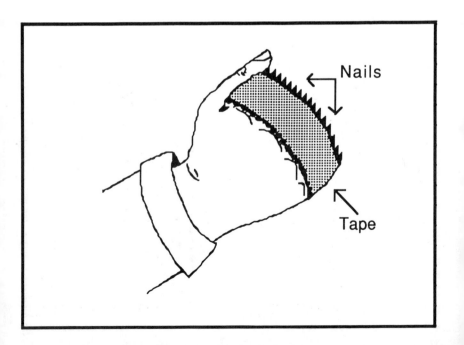

Nail Pen

An ordinary pen modified so that when the top of the pen is turned, a nail about 1/2 inch long is exposed instead of a ball point. The nail can be retracted by turning the top of the pen in the opposite direction. Sharpening the nail provides a more penetrating point.

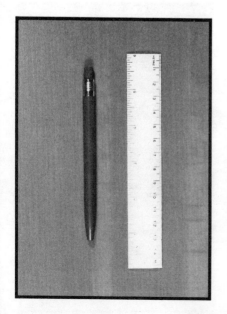
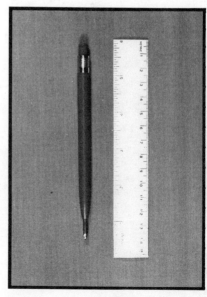

Nail Polish Spike

A bottle of nail polish has its brush removed and replaced with a sharp metal spike approximately 1 inch in length. This spike modification can be made to accommodate virtually any type of make-up applicator.

Necklace Knives

The pendant for an ordinary looking necklace may also be a folding knife. Some of these pendants may be round, square, diamond shaped, or even in the shape of a crucifix. A knife blade of one-inch or shorter in length, frequently made of fine surgical steel, can be easily opened. Closer inspection of necklace pendants is advised, even if they appear to be only religious symbols.

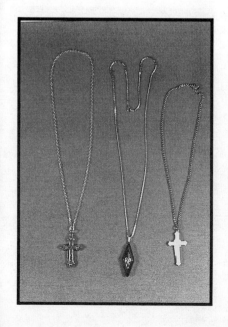

Needle Pens

An ordinary pen can be modified to conceal a hat pin. A fairly thick pen works best since the bead end of the hat pin appears to be a part of the pen itself. The pin's shaft can actually be submersed in the pen's ink.

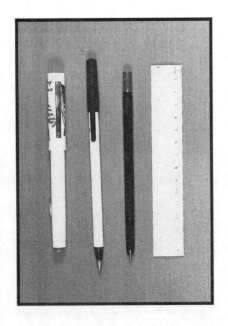 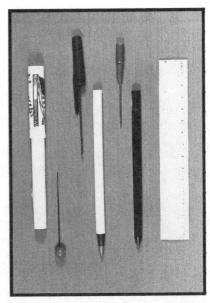

Ninja Claw

There are two different ways this weapon can be used. First, the metal band is worn over the hand and used to enhance punches, in a similar fashion to a set of metal knuckles. Secondly, sharp prongs can be added and worn on the inside of the metal band to puncture or slash at exposed parts of the body. A modified version of this weapon is the "Tiger Claw," which is worn on the index and small finger and used for slashing only.

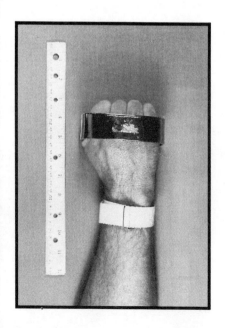
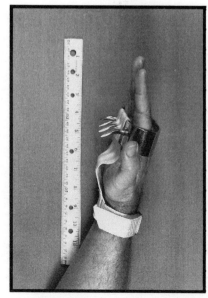

Ninja Knife Forearm Band

A nylon holder that houses three black metal knives is worn on the inside of the forearm and is easily concealed by wearing a long sleeve shirt or jacket. The knife's blades are about three inches long, and with some practice, can be thrown or used for stabbing.

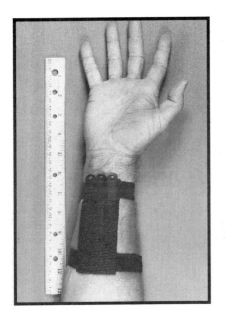 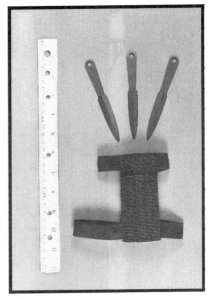

Ninja Needles

A weapon that looks like a cross between a hat pin and an awl. It has a thin metal pointed shaft used to administer puncture wounds. The needles usually range in length from 1 to 2 inches including the small head/handle for holding.

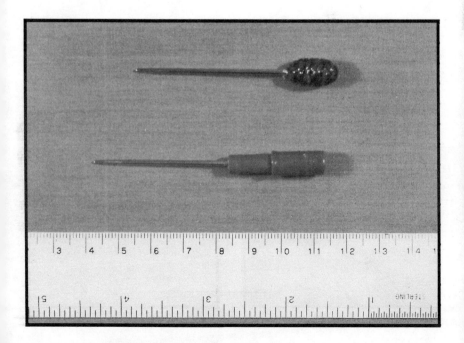

Ninja Needles Kubotan

A keychain that appears very similar to the "Kubotan Keychain Knife," except when the device is unscrewed. Inside is up to 4 black metallic Ninja needles usually 4 inches in length. These Ninja needles can be thrown, although it usually takes a great deal of practice to achieve any accuracy, or they can be used to puncture when held in the hand.

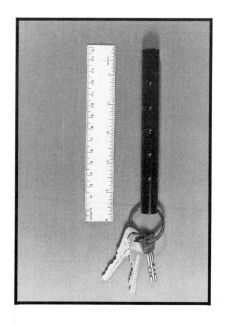 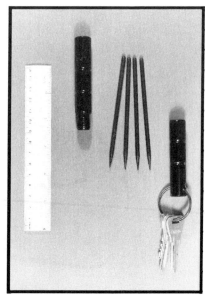

Ninja Spiked Fist Band

A black leather fist band that features steel studs which can enhance the effect of a punch. The steel studs can also penetrate and tear flesh if the strikes are delivered with enough power. A modified version of this weapon, the metal studded wrist band, is frequently worn by "outlaw" type motorcycle gang members, Satanists, and "Heavy Metal" rock music enthusiasts.

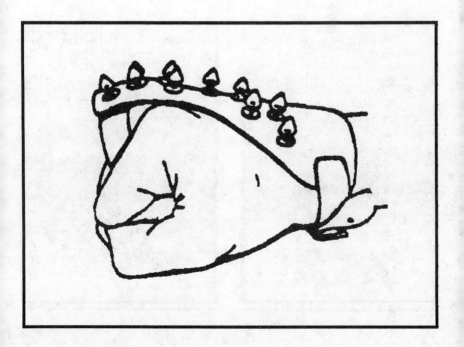

Non-Traditional Opening Knives

There are other knives on the open and "black" markets. These knives have various opening mechanisms and include: gravity fed knives; butterfly knives; thumb opening knives; stiletto type knives; rear handle opening switchblades; and others. These knives can have blades that range from under an inch to several inches long. Some of these knives may be legal to possess in certain states and others may not.

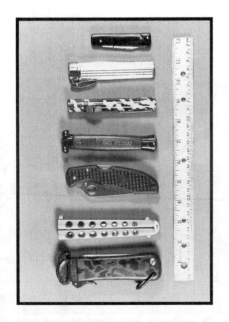 

Pen and Pencil Set
Butterfly Knife

When clipped to a shirt pocket, this device looks like an attractive and quality made matching pen and pencil set, although neither function as writing instruments. This set is actually the handle of a butterfly knife blade that can be quickly and easily opened with a little practice. The blade is approximately 2 1/2 inches in length.

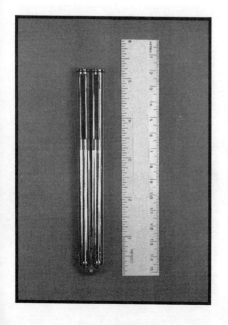
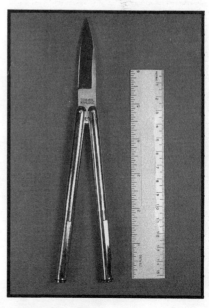

Pen Butterfly Knife

A non-functioning pen, usually silver colored, which is actually a butterfly knife. By moving the top of the pen downward, the butterfly knife blade is exposed and each half of the pen separates to serve as a handle for the blade. The blade is approximately 4 inches in length.

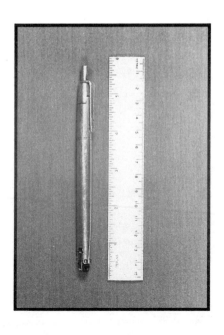 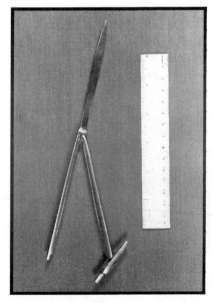

Pen Knives

Pen knives may look slightly different from each other, but they all have one thing in common — they all look like pens. These pens are specifically designed to resemble and function as ordinary pens, except that hidden within each pen is either a pointed metal shaft, or a blade. Most are exposed be removing the cap of the pen. The blades or shafts range from under an inch to several inches long.

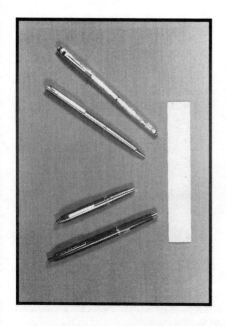
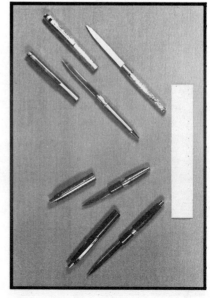

Pocket Clip Folding Knife

When worn in the shirt pocket this knife looks like some type of marking pen. It is actually a folding pocket knife with a blackened metal blade approximately 2 1/2 inches in length.

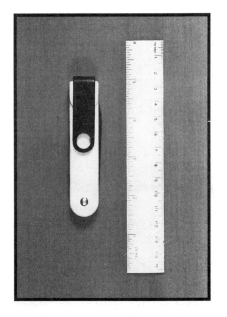
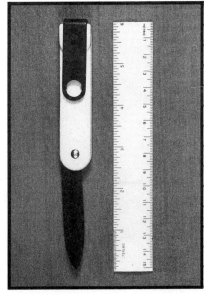

Pop Open Knife on Lanyard

A small, light weight knife that can be comfortably and discreetly worn around the neck on a lanyard type cord. The handle and sheath are made of hard plastic, while the blade is black metal and about 2 inches long.

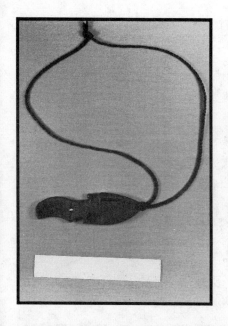
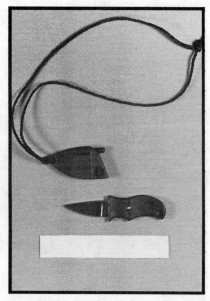

Push Dagger Buckle

A rectangular, black plastic belt buckle with a silver colored, metallic insert suitable for engraving initials, or as a surface for gluing small ornamentation. The harmless looking buckle serves as a sheath for a double-edged push dagger with a 1 inch blade.

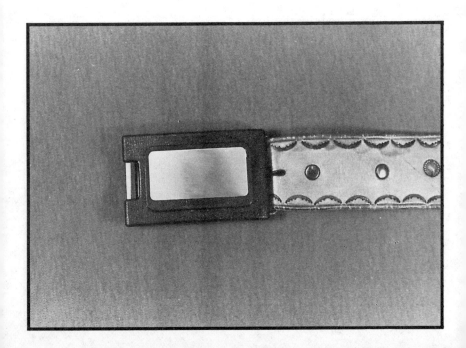

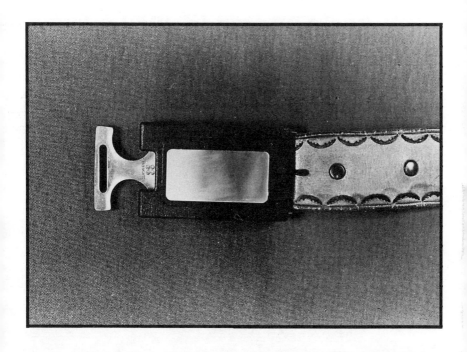

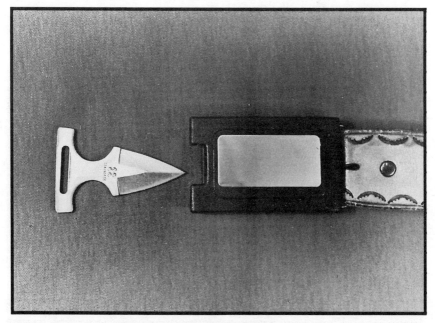

Push Dagger in Wallet

On one side this wallet looks just like a plain leather wallet. The other side, however, holds a 1 1/2 inch double-edged push dagger in a built-in sheath. When the wallet is handed to someone with the dagger side down, the push dagger can easily slide covertly into the hands of the person offering the wallet.

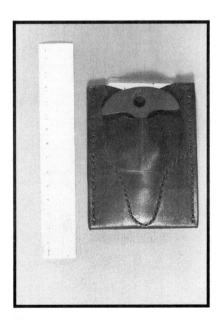
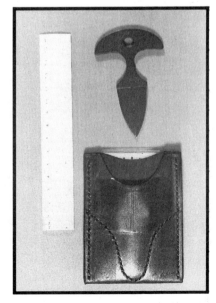

Rattlesnake Bracelet Knife

A Mexican produced weapon worn around the wrist as a bracelet and made from the stiff skin of a rattlesnake. The bracelet can be easily removed from the wrist and straightened into a knife.

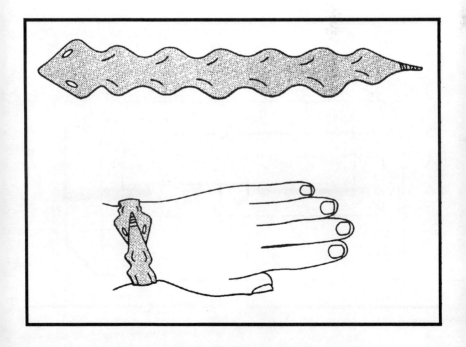

Razor Knuckles

A homemade weapon that can have devastating effects when used to punch. A set of wood knuckles, without individual finger holes, are fashioned with grooves on the top part facing away from the top of the knuckles. Usually four single edged razor blades are inserted in the grooves. This weapon can deliver severe lacerations with each punch.

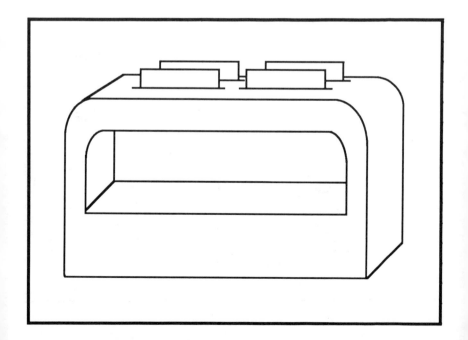

Ready Edge

A spear pointed, 2 inch stainless steel blade knife that features a serrated edge for cutting almost anything. The knife's checkered handle has a soft rubberized feel with double hand guards. The plastic sheath has a quick release lock and a clip that affixes to a keychain, lanyard, or belt loop.

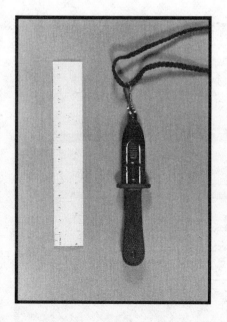
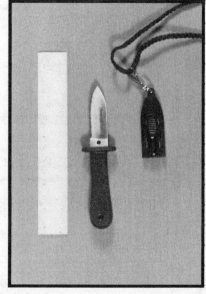

Riding Crop Sword

Similar to a sword cane, the riding crop contains a steel shaft approximately 18 inches in length with a sharp pointed end. When this weapon is among other riding equipment, it could easily go unnoticed.

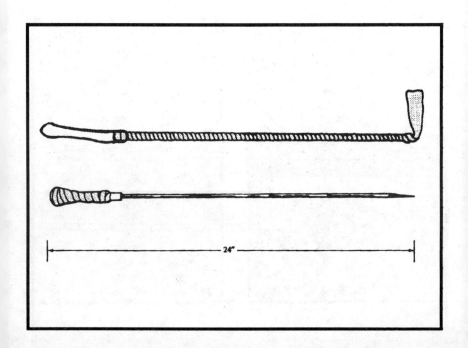

Ruler/Letter Opener

Actually a ruler with a letter opener inside. The only noticeable difference is the separation in the center of the ruler. The six inch ruler has a metal blade approximately 5 inches long, which can be sharpened.

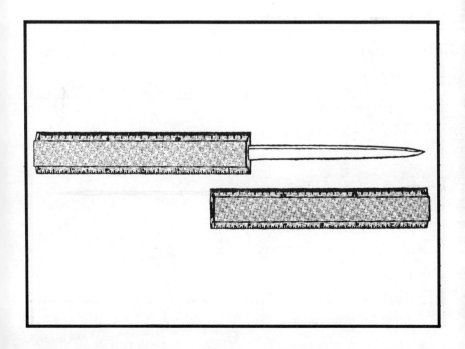

Sharpened Keys

Sharpened keys are usually sharpened using one of two methods. The first method of sharpening is on an ordinary key that has already been cut from a blank. The second method of sharpening is done on a blank key, which has a uniform surface for sharpening. Keys can be sharpened on one side, or both, and made extremely sharp.

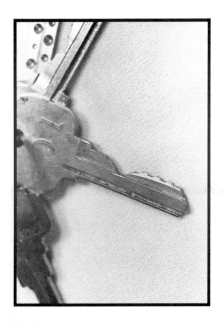

Sharpened Sunglasses

The stems on a pair of sunglasses are sharpened and pointed for the purposes of cutting and stabbing. The sharpened plastic can also be easily serrated to enhance the ripping effect. The party wearing the sunglasses can nonchalantly remove the sunglasses for rapid use. The sharpening can also be performed on an ordinary pair of eyeglasses.

Shell Casing Knife

A weapon usually made from a .30-06 or .308 shell casing. A knife blade can be embedded into the base of a bullet with molded lead. The lead portion can then be inserted into the shell casing with the knife blade concealed, or it can be reversed with the shell's casing used as a handle.

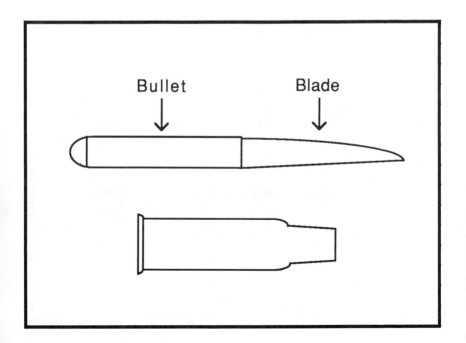

Shotgun Shell Knife

A folding style pocket knife that looks like an ordinary red colored 12 gauge shotgun shell, complete with a high brass casing. A thumb groove opens the 2-inch hardened steel blade.

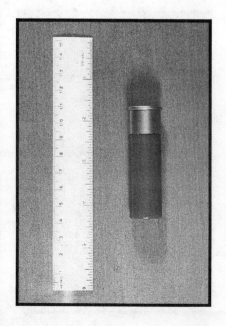
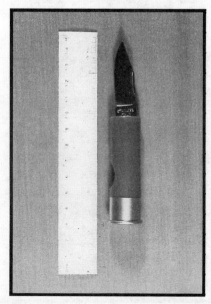

Sliding Blade Keychain

A type of keychain that is usually all metal and approximately three inches long. A two inch blade is locked opened by pushing forward with the thumb. This knife can be opened very quickly and looks non-threatening in the hand when not open.

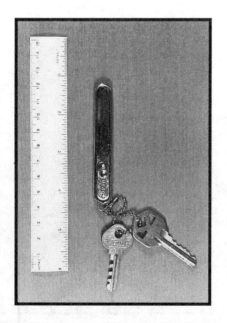
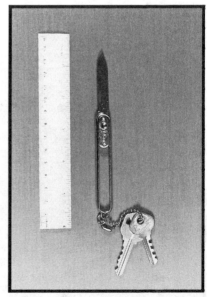

Spike Pods

These homemade spike pods are usually about 2 inches in length. They can puncture tires or the soles of shoes if on a hard surface.

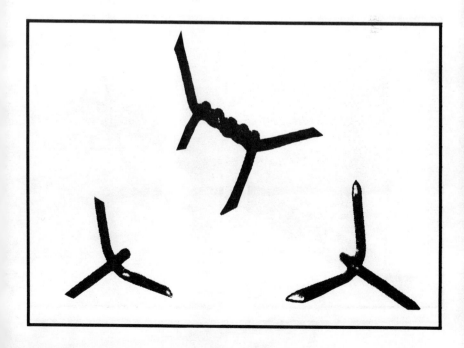

Steel Porcupine

A 36 inch long cane featuring a special handle that, when pulled, allows six sharp metal spikes to snap out. The cane is held by the other end so that it can be swung like a mace, and punctures and tears flesh with each strike. The spikes are completely concealed when carried as a normal cane.

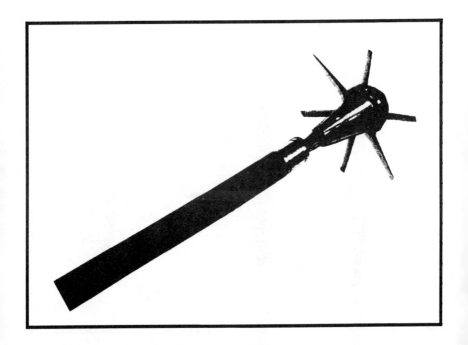

Stiletto Pen

It looks like an ordinary marking or fountain pen when carried in the pocket, but it contains a button that, when pushed forward, exposes a steel blade through spring activation. This spring firing mechanism is so powerful that the blade can pierce human flesh if held against the body when the button is activated. The 2 1/2 inch blade is retracted simply by pushing the button back.

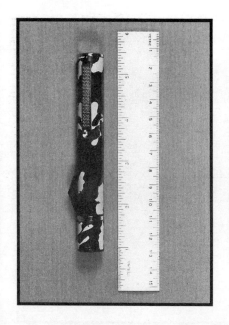 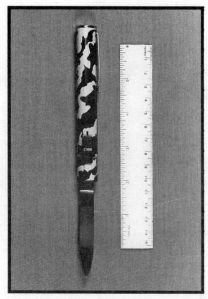

Survival Tool Wallet

A commercially available device that looks like a small black wallet, but when the wallet is unsnapped and opened, a slashing weapon is revealed. This weapon features a hole for the middle finger with opposite side grooves for the index and ring finger so it can be used in a brass knuckle fashion. The weapon's double-edged 2 inch blade offers the option of either a serrated edge, or a razor edge as the cutting surface. This device has also been marketed as an ice scraper.

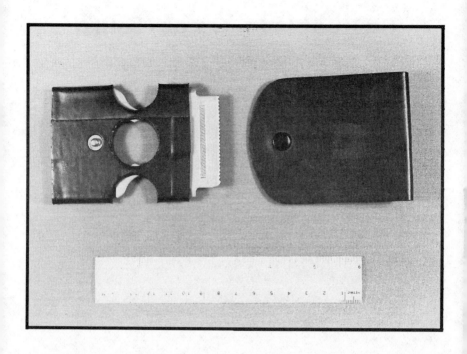

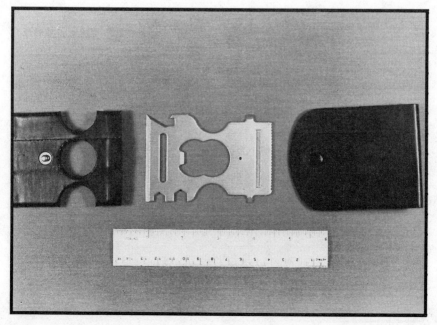

Switchblade Comb/Knife

A modified version of the legal and commercially available switchblade comb, except that the comb has been removed from its metal frame and replaced with either two single-edged razor blades, or a cut-down blade from a jig-saw. The blade can be up to 3 inches long.

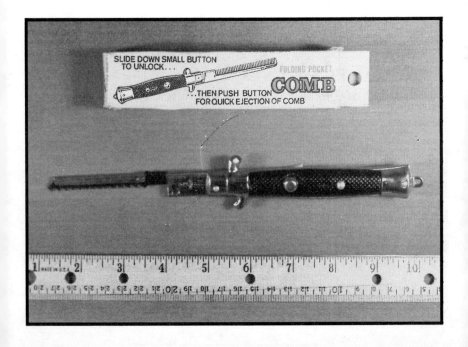

Sword Canes

A weapon that comes in various sizes and shapes. They all have at least one thing in common — a hidden blade. Most sword canes are manufactured in India, and vary in quality from poor, to excellent.

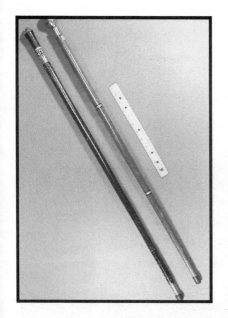
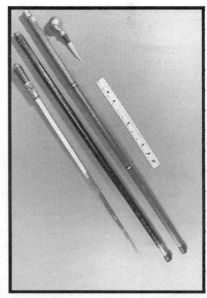

Sword Umbrella

A fully functioning folding umbrella conceals a ten-inch round and pointed surgical steel blade hidden inside the telescoping umbrella. A unique double locking system makes it very difficult to detect the presence of the blade, yet it allows quick access for the user. The sword's point can easily penetrate most soft body armor.

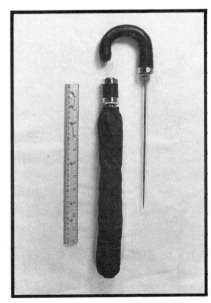

Tekna Security Card

A weapon that is approximately the hcight and width of a common credit card, but slightly thicker. It features a thumb-button opening and locking device that produces a 2 inch long hardened, stainless steel blade. This card has been advertised, "Awaits your commands for those highly specialized tasks. But unlike other cards, the security card is the personal card that won't charge you interest."

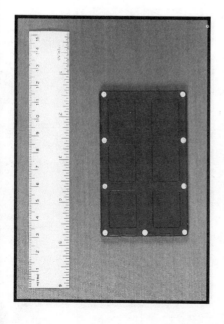
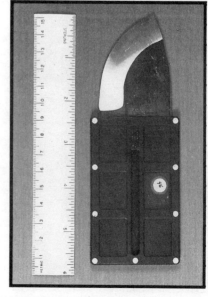

Three to Six Blade
Throwing Star

A weapon carried in a leather pouch and worn on the belt. The three points are actually double points that can be made into six by sliding the metal points open. These six points are now locked open with spring pressure and ready for throwing.

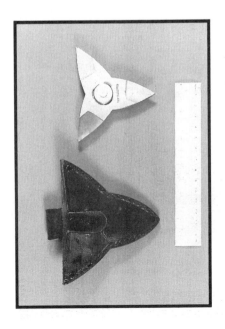
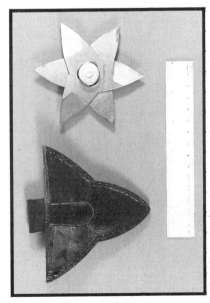

Throwing Darts

Generally not thought of as weapons, throwing darts can be very effective puncturing weapons. Darts can be held in the hand, or thrown, and can be particularly effective when thrown down from a high place, such as a multiple story building. When darts are thrown downward, the weighted point strikes first.

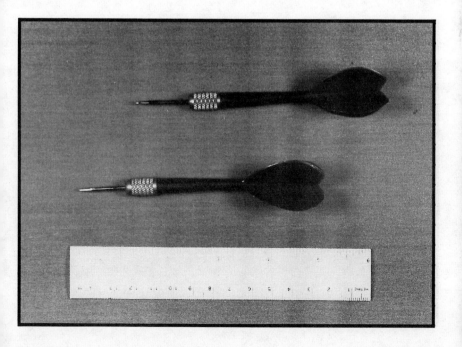

Throwing Stars

Available in most Martial Arts stores and catalogs, throwing stars come in a variety of sizes and shapes. Most of them have sharp points, and some can have extremely sharp edges. These weapons can either be thrown, or used as hand-held weapons.

Watch Cat

A device that is being marketed as a self-defense keychain. Made of aluminum, this weapon looks like the face of a cat and can be held in the hand to strike and puncture. The eyes are a prime target area of attack since the cat's pointed ears are about the width of human eye sockets.

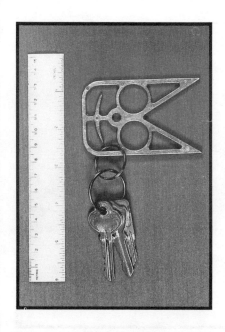
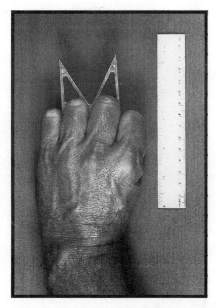

Whip Stabbing Device

An ornamental whip that features a handle which conceals a metal ice pick type shaft. The shaft is approximately 4 inches long.

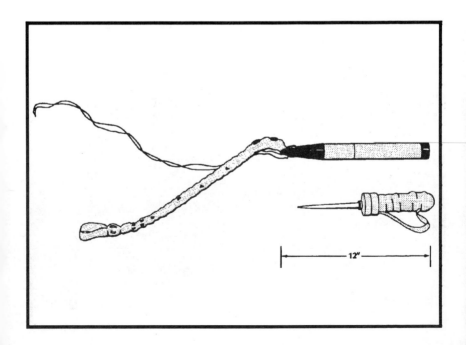

World War I Trench Knife

A "knuckle knife" that can be used for punching (with the knuckles), or for stabbing (with the blade). If held in a dagger grip, the knife's 7 inch long blade can easily be concealed along the arm, and will appear as though only a pair of brass knuckles are being worn.

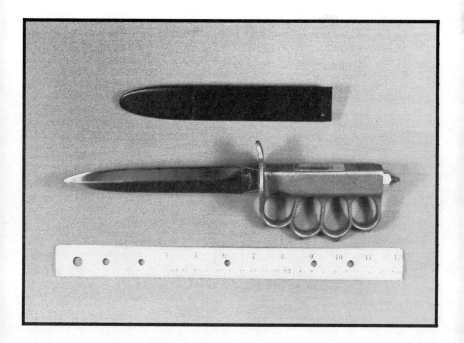

Yawara Knife

A knife that is similar in appearance to the "Kubotan Keychain Knife," but this knife is larger with a total of length of 8 inches. This knife can be used as an impact or control weapon when closed, or by simply unscrewing it, a knife with a 3 1/2 inch blade is available.

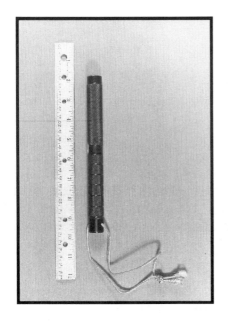 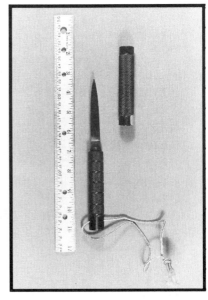

Section Two:

Firearms

"A fool sees not the same tree that a wise man sees"

— William Blake

This section includes firearms that are both homemade and commercially manufactured. A few of the commercially manufactured firearms are quite small. Some homemade firearms appear crude, and may not even resemble firearms. However, they can be just as deadly. But all the firearms shown in this section fit the definition of a firearm. This section also includes information on how many of these firearms can be covertly carried, whether on the human body, or in other locations.

Altered Handlebar Shotgun

A 12 gauge shotgun occasionally used by members of "Outlaw" type motorcycle gangs. A motorcycle handlebar end serves as the muzzle of the shotgun, which is manually fired by depressing a button that releases a spring loaded firing pin, driving it into the shotgun shell's primer. A modified version of this weapon has a small electrical solenoid inserted into the handlebar, which can be fired by depressing a button with the hand or foot.

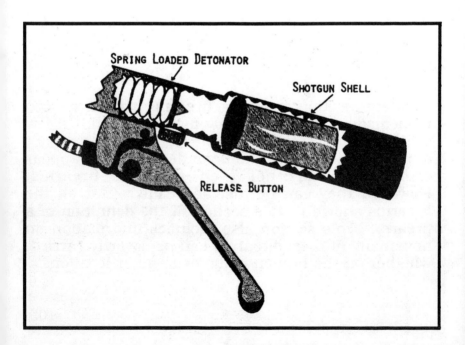

Athletic Support Concealment

A small handgun can be secured in the compartment in an athletic support that holds the protective cup. Wearing the protective cup over the firearm, although it may be somewhat uncomfortable for extended periods of time, greatly adds to the concealability of the firearm.

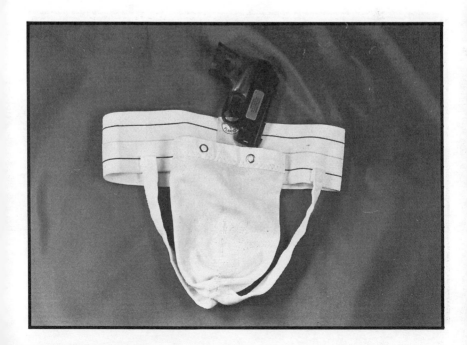

Baby Browning in
Gun Wallet Holster

This miniscule .25 ACP "Baby Browning" fits snugly and sits flat when carrying it in this wallet holster in the back pocket. The firearm should, however, be removed from the wallet holster for proper firing.

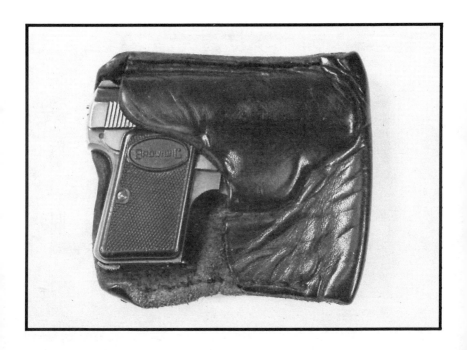

Belt Mounted Gun

A 4 1/2 inch long, homemade device usually attached to the belt and able to fire two .38 caliber cartridges. The weapon is typically fired by connecting one end of a piece of string or wire to the firing pin of the weapon, and threading the other end through a coat sleeve and tying this end around a finger. The weapon can be easily fired when a person puts their hands up, or against a wall.

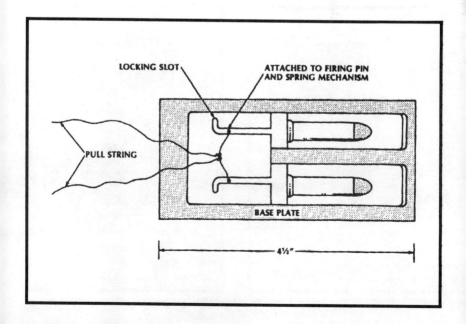

Beretta Holster Gun Wallet

A holster wallet that snaps closed over a small Beretta .22 caliber or .25 ACP auto pistol. A hole through both sides of this holster allows multiple shots to be fired from the Beretta while the holster is still closed. There is also another version of this holster that will allow the firing of a High Standard .22 Magnum (WMR) Derringer or similar models.

 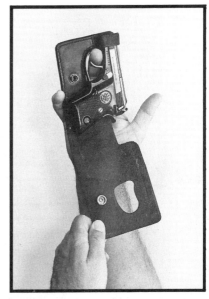

Billy Club Shotgun

A firearm, resembling a billy club, and made of metal, 1 inch in diameter and 9 inches long. The barrel is covered with hard black rubber. The grip end is unscrewed to load a single 16 gauge shotgun shell. A sliding button serves as the weapon's triggering device. Length varies, and one model can fire a .12 gauge shell, and another a .44 magnum.

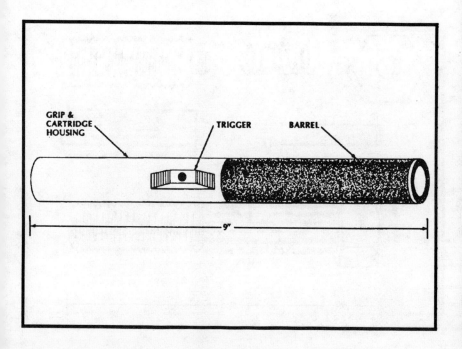

GRIP & CARTRIDGE HOUSING   TRIGGER   BARREL

9"

Bolt Gun

A modified bolt that looks no different in its outward appearance than a non-modified bolt. This gun is homemade from a 4 1/2 inch long, and 5/8 inch in diameter, standard machine bolt that can fire a .22 caliber short, long, or long rifle cartridge. The weapon is loaded by unscrewing the threaded portion of the bolt, which acts as the barrel, and placing a "live" cartridge inside. Pulling back and releasing the hexagonal bolt head fires the weapon.

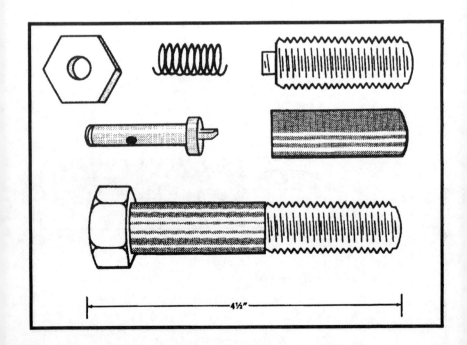

Cane Gun

Closer inspection of an ordinary looking walking cane may reveal that it is actually a "Cane Gun." This smooth bore, single shot .36 caliber percussion weapon is fired by removing the top metal part of the cane. Releasing a spring-loaded screw on the handle which strikes the firing cap, causes detonation. Since this is a black powder firearm, it may not be subject to the same restrictions as most other firearms.

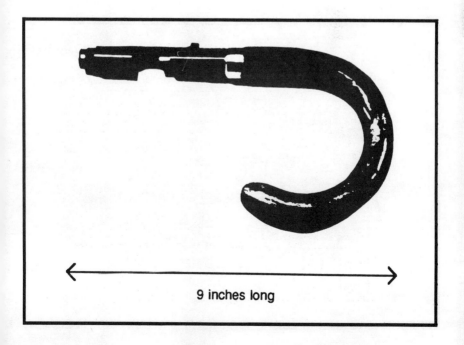

9 inches long

Car Door Shotgun

Supposedly designed specifically to kill law enforcement officers, a modified shotgun is shortened and placed inside the door of a vehicle. One end of a wire is attached to the shotgun's trigger and the other end to the dashboard of the vehicle. This enables the driver to open the door and fire the shotgun without getting out of the vehicle, or turning around. Side mirrors on vehicle doors can be used to aim the weapon.

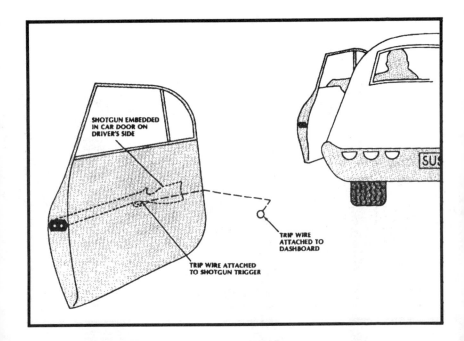

Double Barrelled Firearm

A device that closely resembles a cigarette lighter and can be easily concealed in the hand or pocket. Two .25 caliber cartridges can be fired, either independently, or at the same time. The weapon is loaded by unscrewing the two barrels and placing the "live" cartridges into the threaded ends. The barrels are screwed back in, and the weapon is fired by pulling back and releasing the two small pins, which can be locked back in a firing position.

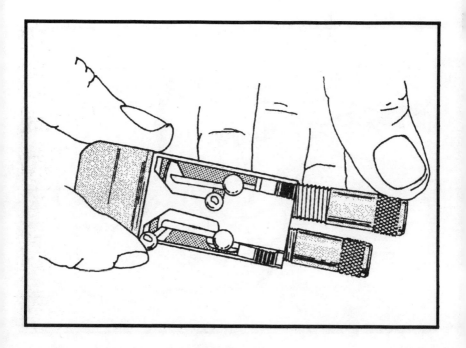

Dual-Purpose Cigarette Lighter

A common looking cigarette lighter contains a lighter, but also a .22 caliber single-shot firearm. This dual-purpose lighter is homemade from plans that are commercially available in various magazine ads.

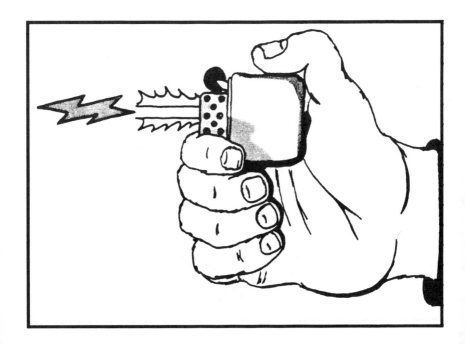

Equalizer Ring Gun

A bulky looking ring containing a miniature gun that can actually fire .22 caliber long rifle ammunition on a manually reloaded, single shot basis. A tiny handle on the ring's left side cocks the gun and reveals the retractable barrel on the side, so that firing can take place by simply depressing a lever with the thumb. The small barrel then goes back into the rings body, which is concealed by the spring-loaded side flap.

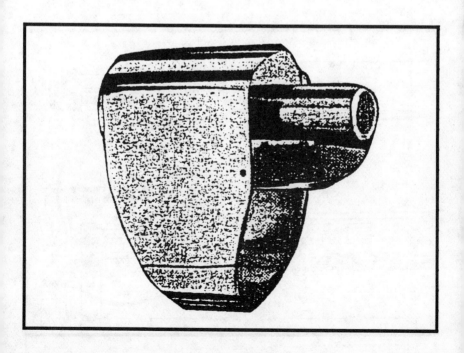

Electrical Connector Shotgun

A shotgun fashioned from an electrical connector and designed to fire a 12 gauge shotgun shell. This small device can be concealed in a long glove, the type frequently worn by "outlaw" type motorcycle gang members.

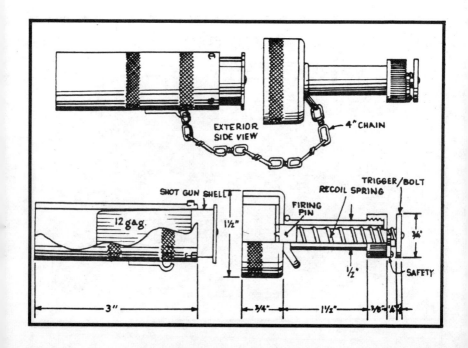

Firing Jewelry

Functioning firearms, which are typically cuff links, tie clasps, charms, and pendants, are approximately 1 1/2 inches in length and resemble miniature antique pistols. The pistols are usually loaded with a small charge of number 8 or 9 birdshot, and can deliver fatal shots at close range.

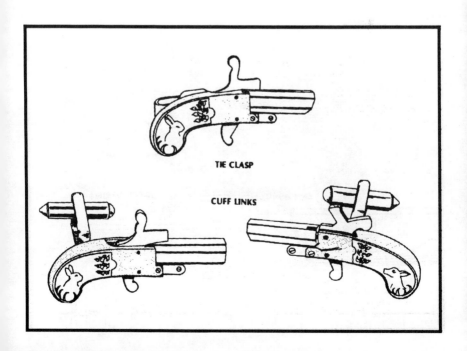

TIE CLASP

CUFF LINKS

Hide-A-Gun

A device that allows a handgun to be securely concealed under the dash of an automobile, a table, or virtually any type of hard flat surface. The device has no straps and allows the knowledgeable user to have quick access to a handgun from a secure hiding place.

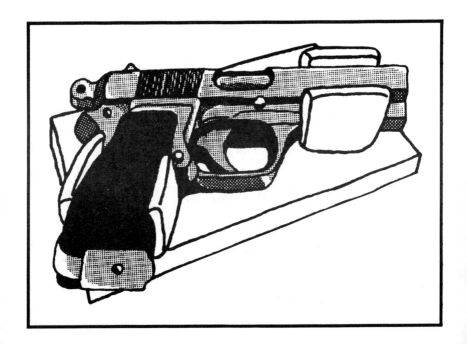

Highway Flare Shotgun

A homemade shotgun wrapped in red paper to resemble a highway flare. Closer inspection reveals that the "flare" is larger in diameter and that the paper is a different texture than that of a conventional highway flare. In order to fire this shotgun, the smaller pipe is pointed at the target, while the outer pipe is firmly held in the hand or rested against a firm object. The smaller pipe is "pumped" to the rear, causing the firing pin to strike the primer which fires the shell.

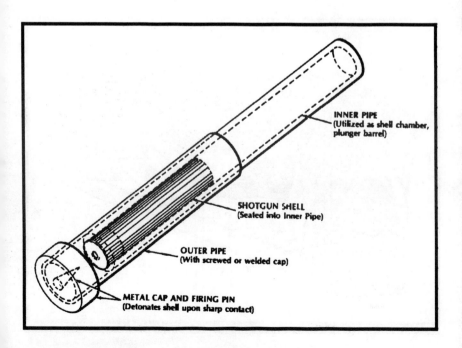

Jewelry Box with Gun Booby Trap

A device that can be designed to fire in two basic ways. The first way is to rig the trigger of a small handgun in a trip wire fashion, so that when the bottom drawer on the jewelry box is pulled open, the gun fires and discharges a round of ammunition in whatever direction the gun is aimed. The second way uses a trip wire that is tightened when a built-in music box is played, and the tightened wire fires the gun.

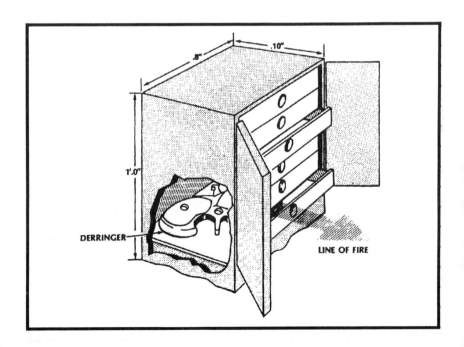

Keychain Gun

A keychain gun that consists of a metal cylinder and a rock attached to a key ring. It fires a .22 caliber cartridge which is placed in the key ring end of the metal cylinder/barrel. The weapon is fired, although somewhat crudely, by firmly striking the cartridge head with the rock.

Knife Gun

A device with the capability to both cut, and shoot. This ordinary looking, single-blade, folding pocket knife is also able to fire a .22 caliber cartridge. One moving part slides out of the handle and accepts a cartridge. The other moving part inside the handle cocks against a small spring and, when lightly squeezed, snaps forward and strikes the cartridge. The barrel of the firearm follows the knife's blade.

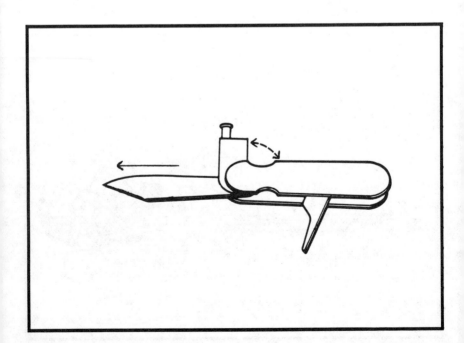

Krupp K.K. Super Weapon

A single-shot .357 Magnum firearm that can easily be concealed when held in the hand. This weapon is not easily recognizable as a firearm and is supposed to make substantially less noise than a standard handgun. It also has no vertical recoil, and can be fired under water.

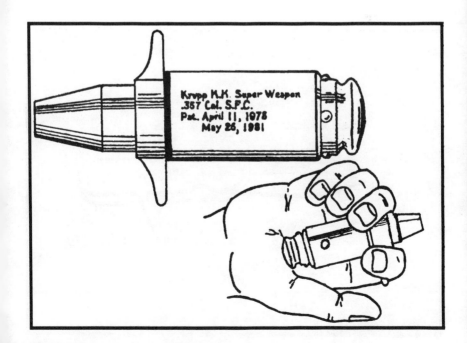

Leg Wallet Holster

An elastic band featuring a large pocket that can be worn around the lower part of the leg, and frequently used to conceal valuables or contraband. It can also be used to securely conceal a small handgun in a somewhat similar fashion to a traditional ankle holster.

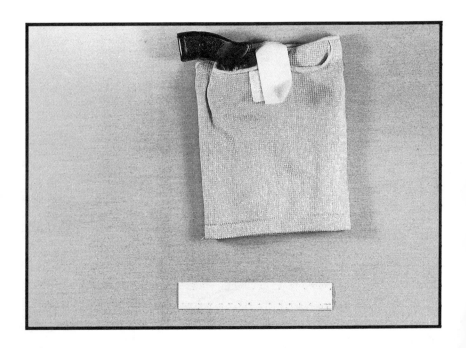

Loaded Armrest

A concealed storage space found in the armrest of some vehicles that can be easily accessed by removing the screw securing the armrest to the console. This area is large enough to fit a short barrelled, medium framed revolver, or auto pistol.

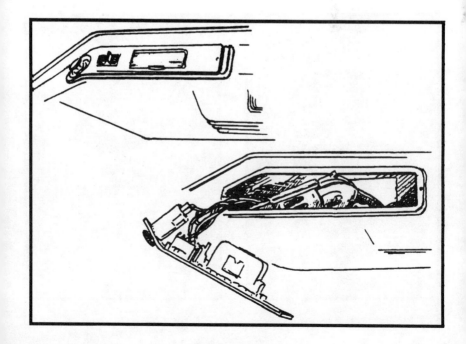

Magazine Shotgun

Virtually any gauge shotgun shell can be used to make a crude shotgun by gluing a BB, or small ball bearing, to the shotgun shell's primer and inserting the shell into one end of a rolled-up magazine secured with rubber bands. All that is needed to fire the shell is to strike the BB on a hard object and point the other end toward the intended target. Effectiveness of this weapon is increased by first placing the shell in a small and properly fitting piece of pipe.

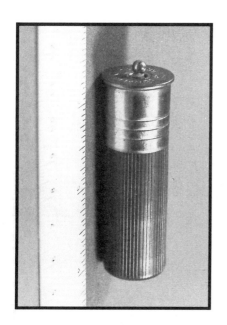
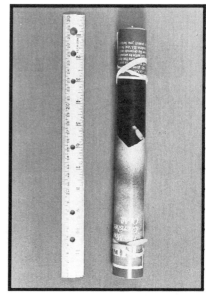

Mini-Revolvers

Miniscule single-action revolvers are about the smallest multiple shot firearms ever manufactured that can accommodate commercially available ammunition. The two best known manufacturers are North American Arms and Freedom Arms. They usually hold five rounds of ammo in the cylinder with one or more of the following rounds: .22 short; .22 long; .22 long rifle; and, .22 Magnum (WMR). Barrel lengths range from 1 to 2 1/2 inches in length.

Mini-Revolver Buckle

A commercially manufactured buckle specifically made to accommodate a mini-revolver on the buckle's face. Just a push of a small button on the face of the buckle allows the firearm to pop into the hand. The mini-revolver easily snaps back into the buckle. It was reported that a person could not be charged with "carrying a concealed handgun" when wearing the mini-revolver buckle, since the mini was not concealed.

Mini-Revolver in Cigarette Box

A 1 inch barrelled .22 caliber short mini-revolver can easily fit into a crush proof cigarette box. The box still has room for a few cigarettes in addition to the mini.

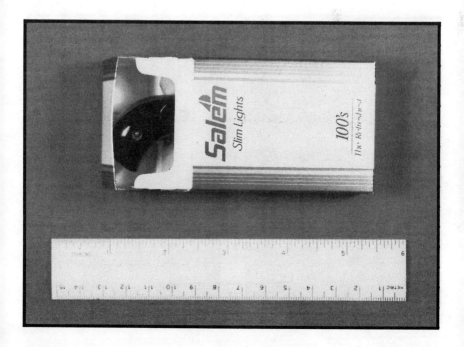

Mini-Revolver in Glove

A mini can easily be concealed in a glove or mitten. The mini fits very comfortably in the palm of the hand, and may be difficult to see when bulky gloves or mittens are worn, particularly in cold weather.

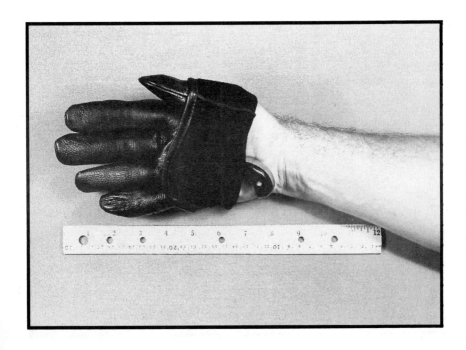

Mini-Revolver in Hat

A knit stocking hat can be an ideal location to hide a mini-revolver, particularly when the mini is worn in a fold toward the back of the head.

Mini-Revolver in Necktie

A mini-revolver is easily concealed in the body of a necktie by cutting down a .22 caliber bore brush and drilling or modifying a hole in one end to affix to the necktie. The brush can be sewn into the necktie or affixed with a safety pin. The barrel of the mini is inserted onto the end of the bore brush, which will hold the mini securely inside the tie. The mini can be deployed quickly when attached in this manner. This method of concealment can also be used to conceal a mini in other locations on the body.

 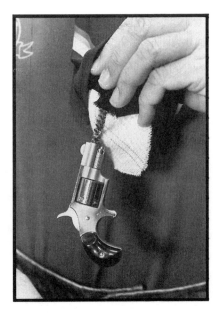

Mini-Revolver Holster/Grip

A holster/grip made by the mini's manufacturer fits comfortably in a pocket, clipped to the belt, or in some other location. The mini can be opened from the closed position by simply pulling the revolver from the holster/grip in a fashion similar to the opening of a folding knife. When open, the holster/grip provides a better hold on the mini, which improves accuracy when shooting.

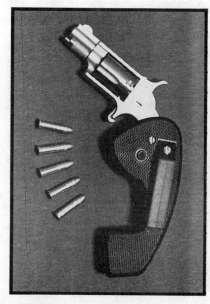

Mini-Revolver Pager Holsters

There are two basic types of pager holsters, and both are somewhat large when compared with today's standard sized pagers. One holster covers the mini-revolver, which is secured with a piece of elastic, and serves strictly as a holster. The pager case is simply pulled down to open, providing rapid access to the mini. When held in the hand, the second holster allows a mechanism to cock and fire the mini while inside the pager. Both of these pager holsters look like authentic pagers even though they are larger.

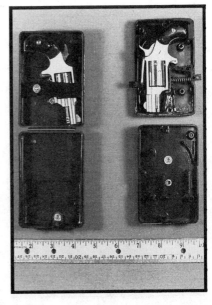

Pen Guns

These commercially manufactured and home-made weapons offer versions that fire anything from a .22 caliber short to a .410 shotgun shell. When sitting in a shirt pocket, they look relatively inconspicuous. They are particularly effective for short range firing. This weapon is cocked and fired by pulling back the spring loaded firing pin knob from its safety rest and releasing it. The "Pen Gun" photo included here will fire a 2 1/2 inch .410 gauge shotgun shell.

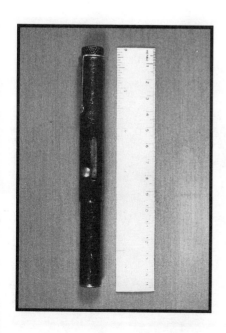
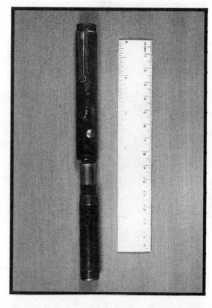

Pipe Shotgun

An effective, cheap, and easy to make home-made single shot pump shotgun that can be made to fire virtually any gauge shotgun shell. A smaller section of pipe that snugly fits the appropriate gauge shotgun shell is selected as the barrel. A slightly larger section of pipe, which allows the barrel to fit into it, serves as the breech. The breech has a nipple end cap that screws over the threaded end. A firing pin is fashioned by either welding a small metal protrusion into the end cap, or the end cap is drilled and a screw is threaded so that enough of the screw protrudes out the other end. The shotgun is fired by rapidly "pumping" the two sections together. Can be made in various lengths.

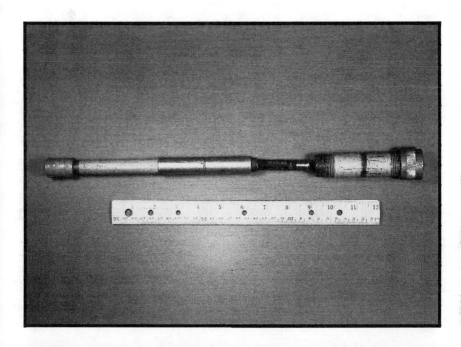

Pouch with Hidden Gun Holster

A pouch that hangs over the belt and used to carry a knife, fingernail clippers, pager, etc., while inside the pants another pouch serves as a holster for a small firearm. To deploy the firearm, the outside pouch is simply lifted, which allows the firearm to be drawn from the previously hidden holster. These pouch/hidden holsters are commercially manufactured, or they can be easily homemade.

Rat Trap Firearm

A homemade "booby trap" firearm that fires .22 Magnum (WMR) ammunition from a modified rat trap. A 2 inch long and 1/2 inch in diameter piece of copper tubing is inserted through the rear at the top of the rat trap. The live cartridge is fitted through a washer to keep the cartridge from sliding into the tubing. Both the washer and the tubing are kept in place with glue or tar. The release mechanism is slightly bent for a firm catch on the spring action, which serves as the hammer. The trap can be secured to virtually any fixed object, such as a tree, about three to five feet above the ground. A camouflaged wire or cord is stretched along a path where the "barrel" is pointed to release the firing mechanism. There have also been found 12 gauge versions of this weapon.

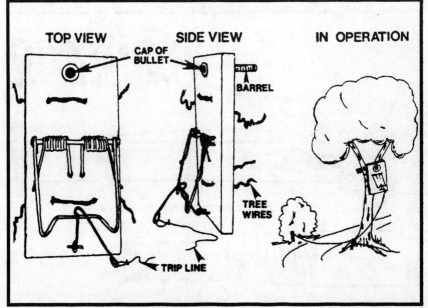

Shark Killer

A homemade weapon made of plastic, brass, and stainless steel. The barrel unscrews from the receiver assembly for loading by placing a shotgun shell into the barrel chamber and is screwed back on the receiver assembly, which will slide back approximately 1/4 inch. The bolt retainer can be pressed down, locking the receiver into a cocked position. The spring loaded receiver assembly is activated by merely pressing the end of the barrel against the target, which forces the bolt up and permits the firing pin to spring forward and strike the shotgun shell primer. This causes the weapon to be fired at point blank range.

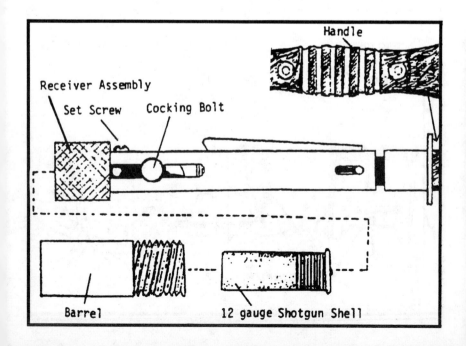

Shirt Tail Holster

A device that attaches to the wearer's shirt tail by means of garter type clips, so that the weapon is hidden below the belt line of the pants. The holster supports a handgun with the gun's butt pointed upward, so that the barrel is horizontal. Small auto pistols are concealed best with this holster, and are quickly accessible.

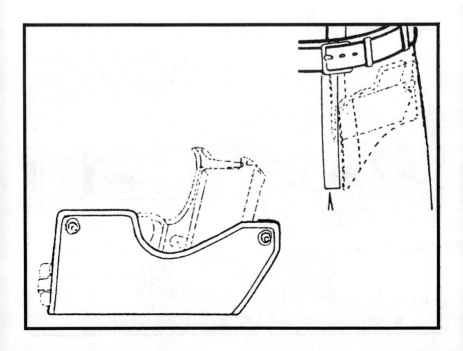

Shock Absorber Shotgun

The shock absorber shotgun typically fires a 12 gauge shell, and can be easily concealed on a motorcycle. The weapon is fired by rapidly forcing the two halves of the shotgun together.

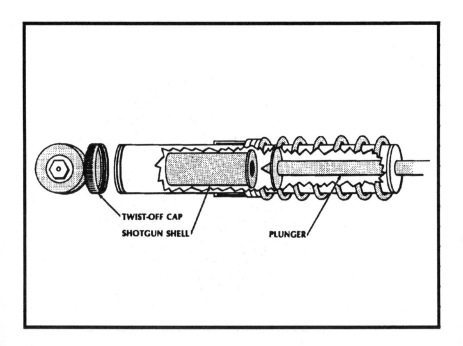

TWIST-OFF CAP

SHOTGUN SHELL

PLUNGER

Shotgun Shovel

A metal shovel handle encased with a spring loaded metal rod and made of 1 inch galvanized pipe, which serves as the firing mechanism. The threaded detachable barrel, usually about 8 inches long, screws onto the handle. The weapon is fired by pulling the spring loaded rod to the rear and releasing it, which strikes the primer and discharges the shotgun shell.

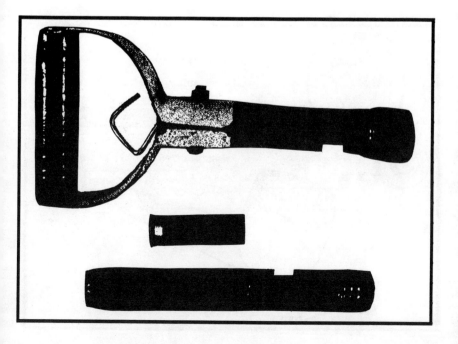

Smoking Pipe Guns

There are two types of these firearms. The first is an ordinary looking smoking pipe that is modified to fire a .22 to .32 caliber cartridge. The pipe stem is bored to allow insertion of a piece of metal tubing to form the barrel of the weapon. The pipe can be fired by pulling back and releasing a small pin on the top of the tube portion of the pipe. The second pipe is constructed so that when the smoker bites down on the trigger button in the stem, the bullet is fired through the front of the pipe's bowl portion.

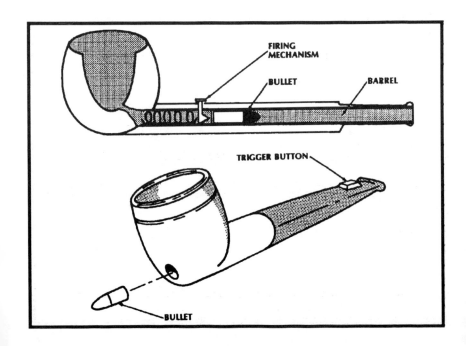

Tire Iron Shotgun

A normal looking tire iron that is capable of firing a .410 gauge shotgun shell. The shell is inserted into the barrel, and the barrel is inserted into the tire iron portion. The weapon is fired by slamming the barrel portion back against the tire iron portion, which has a modified firing pin that strikes the shotgun shell's primer and causes the shell to fire.

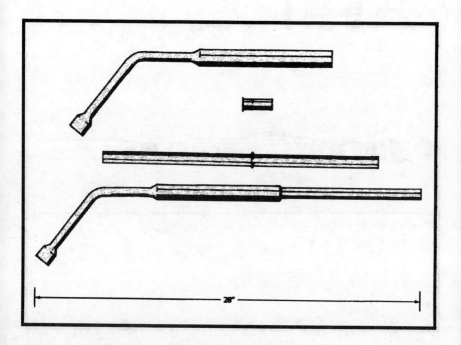

Tire Pressure Gauge Gun

The gauge has been modified to fire any .22 caliber ammunition. In the pocket, or in the tool box, its outward appearance gives little indication that it is a functioning firearm. The weapon is fired by simply cocking and releasing the spring loaded pin on the side of the gauge.

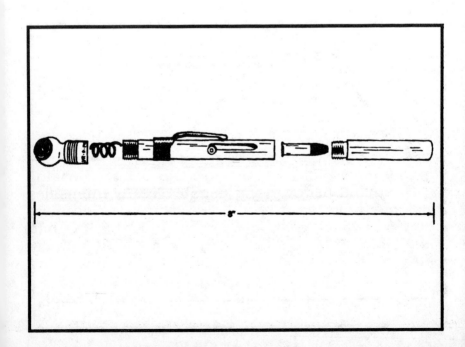

Section Three:

Impact Weapons

"People only see what they are prepared to see."

—Ralph Waldo Emerson

The purpose of this section is to show the various types of weapons designed to be used primarily for striking another human being. Striking with a hand held weapon usually greatly intensifies virtually any unarmed hand strike. The classification of impact weapons include much more than just clubs or batons. It includes special keychains, knuckle devices, weighted gloves, and many other traditional and non-traditional weapons.

149

Automatic Baton

A telescoping spring-action metal baton, also referred to by its martial arts name, the "Tokushu Keibo." With the push of a button, this closed 8 inch baton instantly telescopes to a 20 1/2 inch baton. In addition to using this baton for striking, a strike from the tip when the baton is open can also deliver a severe blow. The baton is closed by tapping the tip on the ground. It is commercially made with a knuckle guard, and includes a leather holster.

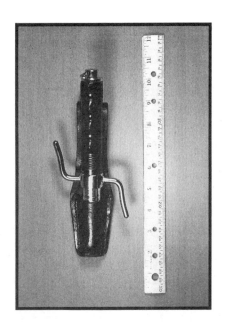 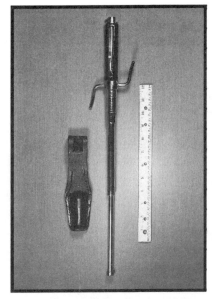

Expandable Keychain

A keychain that is about 5 1/2 inches long when closed, and able to be expanded to about 9 inches when snapped fully open. When closed, the keychain can be used in a similar fashion to the "Yawara" style keychain. It has the extra option of baton type strikes and jabs when the keychain is expanded.

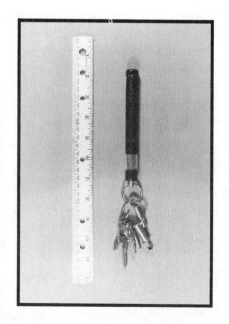 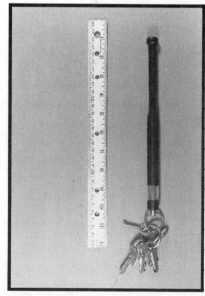

Expandable Straight Batons

Frequently carried by many plain clothes and uniformed police officers, expandable batons come in two models. The "positive lock" model is two sections and firmly locks open with a spring button system. This model, although somewhat larger than the other model, can be easily opened and closed. The "friction lock" model is easier to conceal and usually telescopes open with three sections. This type of baton must be snapped open and pounded on a hard surface to collapse. The "positive lock" models are considered sturdier and more reliable. Collapsed, these batons are 6 to 13 inches long, and expand to 16 to 24 inches in length.

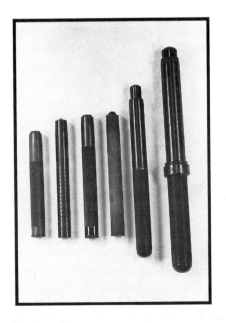

Gunstick

The "Gunstick" (bottom of photo below) has been frequently compared to the "blackjack" (top of photo below). They are, however, used quite differently. The "Gunstick" can be used with the long end up, or in a dagger grip, and is used to strike, jab, or block. The knuckle guard also enhances the effectiveness of punches. The "Gunstick" never really gained popularity, and is rarely carried. The name is deceiving since there is no "gun" in a "Gunstick."

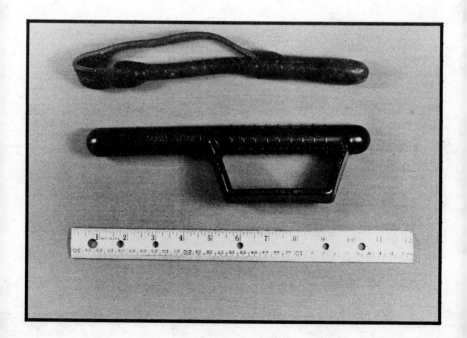

Handler-12 and Scepter Batons

The "Handler-12" baton (top of photo below), looking somewhat like a shortened shepherd's crook, is used to deliver strikes and control techniques. The "Scepter" baton (bottom of photo below) was invented in Canada, and is used in a fashion similar to the PR-24® Police Baton. Both batons can deliver devastating spins and jabs.

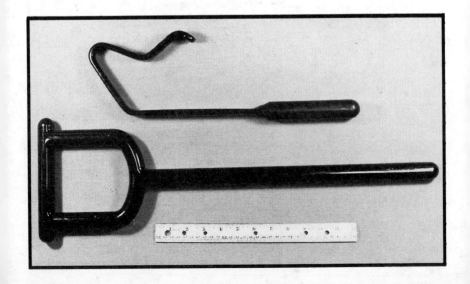

Homemade Clubs

Homemade clubs can be virtually any size and style, and some display a certain degree of ingenuity, such as those pictured below. One (top of photo below) is a homemade style "tomahawk" weapon that has a rock taped to one end for striking, and a leather tong on the other end for holding the weapon in the hand. The other (bottom of photo below) has a piece of heavy metal spring attached to a sturdy, but lightweight, piece of aluminum tubing with a rubber handle. The added weight from the heavy spring enhances the effect of the strikes.

Key Defense Keychain

The "Key Defense Keychain" comes in two models. One is 7 inches long, and the other is 8 1/2 inches long. When closed, they can be used identically to the way "Yawara" style keychains are used. A steel cable attached to the striking head can be snapped out for extra power, adding another 2 1/2 inches. The grooved head can be used to gouge cheeks, eyes, face, groin, etc. Blood, skin, and clothing can also be ripped with the sharpened edges of the grooved head.

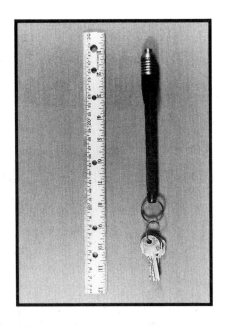
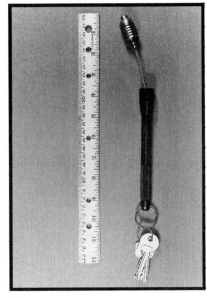

Knockout Cap

A normal looking baseball style, adjustable cap contains about 1/2 pound of powdered lead in the rear of the cap's sweatband. The bill of the cap is held in the hand to deliver "blackjack" type strikes.

Knuckles

Commonly referred as "Brass Knuckles," these devises can be constructed of brass, aluminum, steel, wood, plastic, or virtually any other hard substance. They can either be commercially made, or homemade by a molding process, or through milling and grinding. These weapons can produce devastating effects when used for punching. They are sometimes sold under the guise of being paperweights.

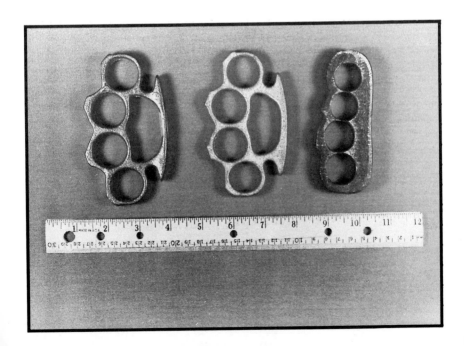

Knuckle Buckle

A standard looking pair of brass knuckles that also serves as a belt buckle. A small protrusion has been added to fit into a hole on the belt. This weapon can be quickly removed from the belt for quick deployment as a set of brass knuckles.

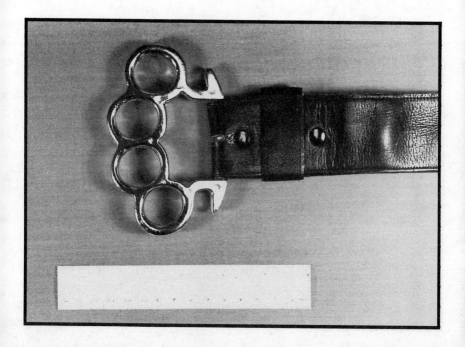

Ninja Shobo

An 8 inch long all metal martial arts weapon that is frequently worn in pairs, with the ring portion sliding over the middle finger on each hand. It can be used to slap, block, and jab. The tapered ends greatly add to the penetration potential of strikes with the ends.

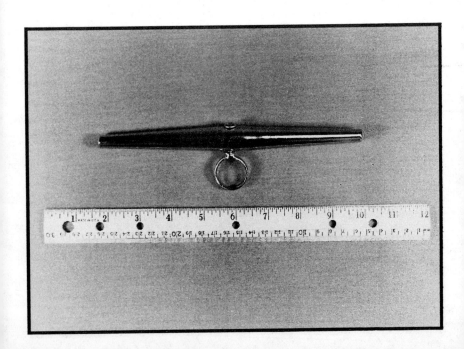

Nunchaku

Most nunchaku are approximately 12 inches in length, usually made of hard wood or a high impact plastic, and connected in the middle with a cord or chain. They can be extremely deadly striking weapons, particularly with the models that have metal studs. They are also used for blocking or control techniques. There are various other models including the "Minichuk" jump rope, which can be used as a jump rope, or in a modified nunchaku fashion. An expandable "extend-a-chuck" version is also available.

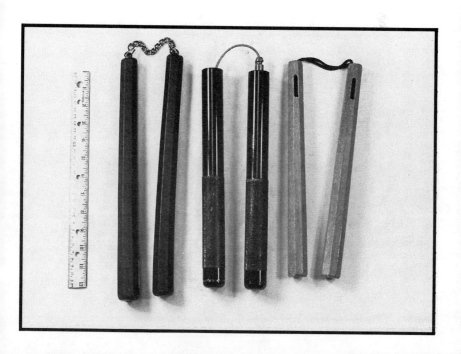

Nunchaku Baton

A baton that appears to be a standard 24 inch aluminum police baton. In fact, it functions rather well as one, and provides the option for use as a nunchaku by simply twisting the baton apart in the middle. The two baton halves are held together by a 4 inch long steel cable. The baton halves also easily fasten back together again.

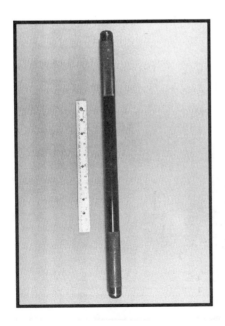
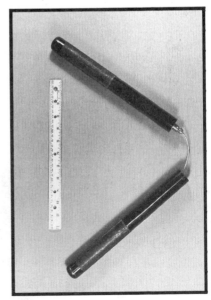

PR-24® Expandable Baton

This baton is an expandable version of the standard PR-24® Police Baton that has been strongly gaining in popularity and acceptance by law enforcement agencies across the nation. It is approximately 13 inches long when closed, and expands to a full 24 inches when opened. This "positive lock" baton can be dynamically or discreetly expanded, and closing is simple. Of course, this type of professional police equipment, like any other, can also fall into the wrong hands.

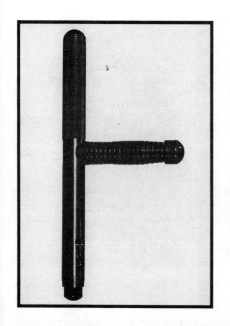
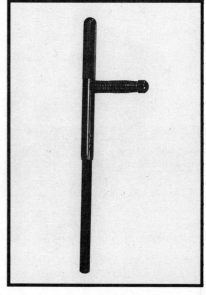

Sap Gloves

Quality made leather gloves that have about 4 ounces of powdered lead sewn into the top knuckle portion on each glove. This lead provides both added weight, and a harder striking surface when delivering punches.

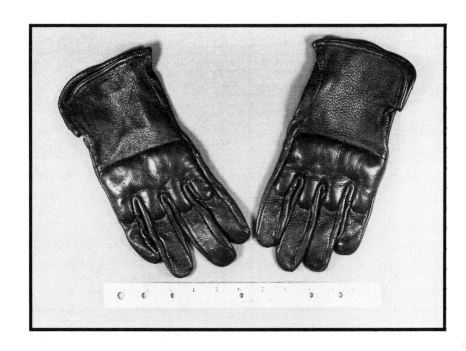

Striking Keychains

Keychains that are used to add effectiveness to strikes. One keychain (left on photo below), known as the "Karate Key," resembles a pair of mini-knuckles and is worn in a knuckle type fashion to deliver enhanced punches. The other keychain (right on photo below) has a slot where the middle finger is placed, and the tapered end is held down. On this model, sometimes known as the "Ninja Keychain," the two protrusions add punching effectiveness, while the tapered end adds focused penetration on hammer-fist type strikes.

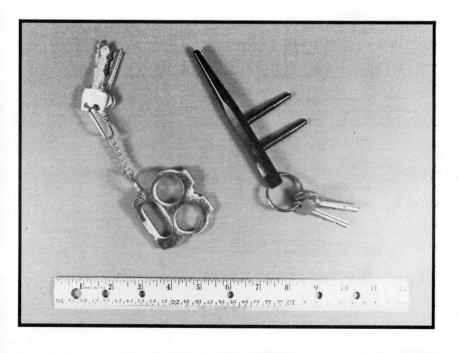

Tonfa

Martial arts weapons that are designed to be used by holding one in each hand. They are usually 18 to 20 inches long, constructed of wood, and can be used to spin, jab, rake, chop, and block. They bear a similar resemblance to the PR-24® Police Baton, but the PR-24® is used in a much different manner.

T-Hold Yawara Stick

This weapon has also been referred to as the "T-Hold Kubotan," and the "T-Hold Mini-Tonfa." This device, when held properly, can intensify the effects of virtually any punch, jab, block or chopping technique. The handle is about 3 1/2 inches high, and the bottom portion is 7 inches long.

Yawara Stick

"Yawara Sticks" come in a variety of styles and shapes. They are usually about 7 inches long and held in the fist. In the hands of a trained person, these weapons can be extremely effective for penetrating type strikes and control techniques to nerve cords or skeletal joints.

Yawara Style Keychains

These keychains can be used to enhance strikes in a similar fashion to using a "Yawara Stick." These weapons are about six inches in length, minus the keychain, and are also known by such names as: "Persuader, Kubotan, and Pow-R Stick." A large number of keys on the end of the keychain make strikes quite effective. A key extender, or an added key ring will also increase the effectiveness of key strikes.

Section Four:

Explosives and Incendiaries

"A danger foreseen is half avoided."

— Thomas Fuller, M.D.

The explosives and incendiaries included in this section are somewhat small, easily concealed or disguised, and simple to make. Explosives are classified as devices that cause damage due to their explosive nature. Incendiaries are devices that use fire as the primary cause of damage or destruction.

NOTE: The authors would like to give a special thank you to Mr. Brian Yerich, President of S.E.T.D., Inc. for his assistance and cooperation in providing information and photos for many of the devices in this section. Law enforcement agencies may seek further information on simulated explosive training devices from S.E.T.D., Inc. in their line of "Training Aids for Law Enforcement." A complete detailed brochure and price schedule of their product line of explosive training devices will be promptly sent. All inquiries should be on department letterhead, and sent to:

S.E.T.D., Inc.
RD #1, Box 53D
Stamford, NY 12167

Aerosol Can Flame Thrower

A device that consists of a pressurized aerosol can that uses an alcohol base as the propellant. The usual is hair spray, which works well. A windproof cigarette lighter with the wick extended is taped just below the nozzle of the can. To ignite the device, the lighter is lit and the nozzle button of the can is pressed at the same time. The flame is generally thrown 3 to 4 feet. When the pressure on the button of the can is released, the flame throwing action stops, and only the lighter is still lit.

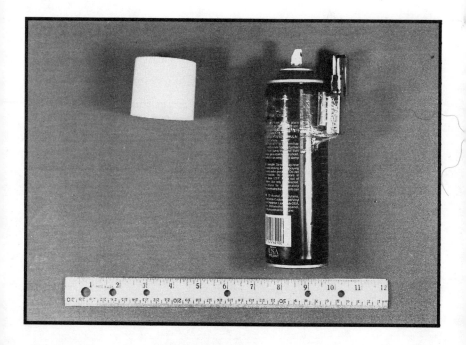

Booby Trapped Shotgun

A device, such as the one illustrated here, was found by police officers and taken to the police station for examination. During the examination it exploded, killing two police officers and injuring two others. The device consisted of six ounces of commercial explosive, an electric blasting cap, three 1.5 volt batteries, one plastic hair curler, two foil contacts and connecting wires, and all contained in the two barrels of the shotgun. When the gun was broken open, the thread pulled the free contact onto the fixed contact, and completed the circuit, causing the device to explode.

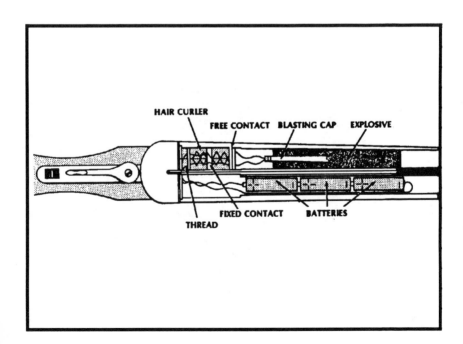

Bookshelf Device

A bomb using plastic explosive. A battery and an electric detonator is placed in a hollowed-out book. Two metal plates are affixed opposite each other on the edge of the pages. Mounted on the bookshelf and hidden by the other books, is a nonconducting divider usually made of thin wood, which cannot be detected by a frontal examination of the books, or shelf. The "loaded" book is placed against the divider, and when the book is removed, the contacts touch, and the device detonates in the hand.

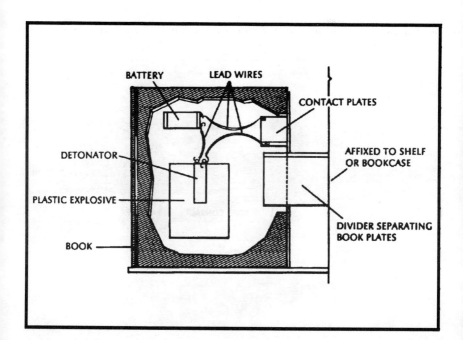

Briefcase Device

This particular device contains six and one-quarter pounds of det-cord primed C-4 plastic explosive, and is initiated by a radio controlled signal. Also incorporated in the wiring circuitry is an anti-handling switch, which triggers the bomb should the briefcase be opened prematurely by an unsuspecting person. With no modifications to the transmitter or receiver, this device can be detonated from up to a mile away.

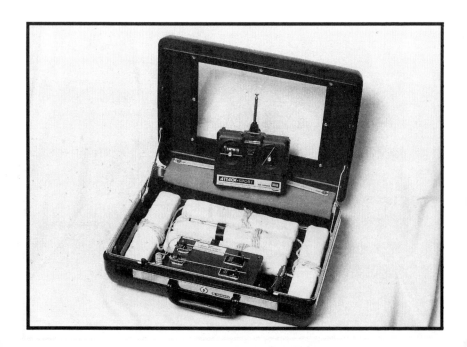

Can with a
Dual Detonation System

This five to ten gallon can device is placed where it can easily be discovered with a burning time fuse projecting from it. Inside the can is a time fuse connected to a detonator in a plastic explosive or dynamite charge. Unseen by the person discovering the device is an internal wire attached to the time fuse and fastened to a pull type detonator, which is also connected to the explosive charge. The normal reaction for anyone is to pull out the fuse. When the fuse is pulled, the device immediately explodes, sending shrapnel and the blast effect outward.

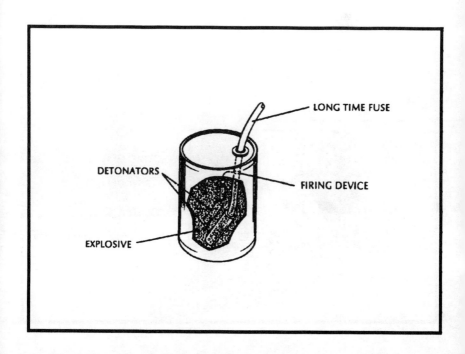

Cartridge Box Bomb

This weapon is frequently used as a boobytrap. A cartridge box with ammunition is used, along with a plastic explosive, electrical detonator, and batteries which are placed and secured in the middle of the box. Two loops of wire, stripped of insulation, are the contact points. Cardboard dividers are affixed to the sections of the bullet holder/tray, and these dividers are each attached to one of the contact wires. The cartridges are replaced in the trays on each end of the box. If the box is opened, only the ammunition is noticed. Sliding the cartridge tray causes the wire and divider to be pulled, thus closing the loops for detonation.

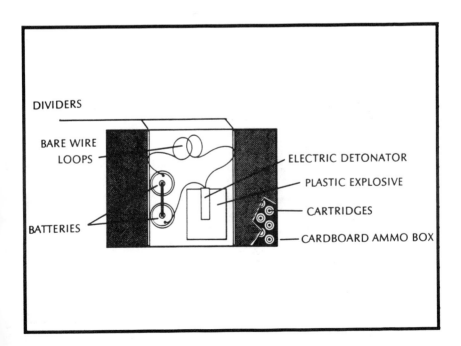

Cassette Player Device

This device uses a audio cassette player with an automatic cutoff capability. A contact point is affixed to the "play" button. A second contact strip is placed over the play button so that when the button rises, i.e., when the tape runs out, or when the stop button is pushed, the two contacts touch and detonate an explosive charge.

Cement Hand Grenade

A plastic explosive, or sometimes TNT, is placed inside a plastic bag or rubber balloon, and a detonator with a time fuse is inserted into the explosive. The plastic bag or balloon is then put in the bottom of a plastic or glass bottle, or can, and cement is poured into the container. The explosive is held in the center of the cement. When the cement hardens, the can, glass, or plastic container can be broken away, but more often it is left in place to add to the shrapnel effect. The device can be thrown, and is effective within a 10 meter area.

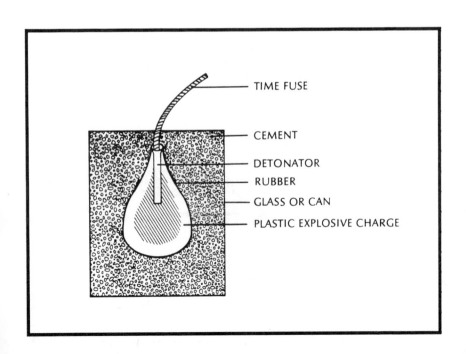

TIME FUSE

CEMENT

DETONATOR

RUBBER

GLASS OR CAN

PLASTIC EXPLOSIVE CHARGE

Cherry Bomb Grenade

A powerful firecracker, such as a "Cherry Bomb" or an "M-80" can be specially modified as a small, but effective hand grenade. The body of the firecracker is coated with glue, then any type of fragments such as tacks, BB's, etc. is stuck to the glue coating. When the firecracker explodes, the explosion has a fragmentation effect that is particularly effective at close range. This gluing concept can be used with most explosive devices.

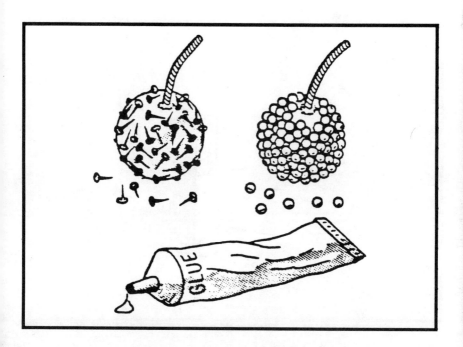

Cigarette Pack Bomb

A typical package of cigarettes is partitioned and a plastic explosive is inserted on one side. A small hole with a projecting time fuse is visible at the bottom. The fuse is very small and usually split to increase its capacity to be lit with a match. The visible cigarettes on one side aid in concealment. It can be tossed on the street, or into a vehicle. The fuse delay is usually 3 to 5 seconds, and has the explosive effect similar to that of a letter bomb.

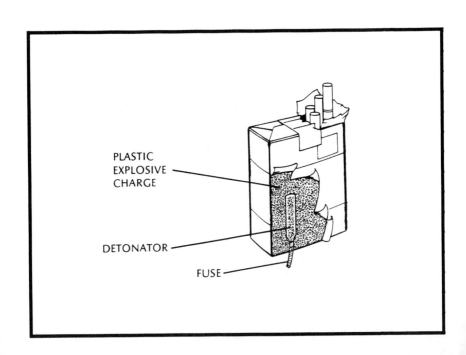

CO^2 Cylinder Explosive

A device constructed from an empty CO^2 cylinder, the type used in many pellet and BB guns, and is about 3 inches long. It is packed with black powder with a fuse-type ignitor. The device can be packed with any type of explosive and uses a variety of fusing or detonation systems. It is a small and easy to conceal device, that can also be very powerful.

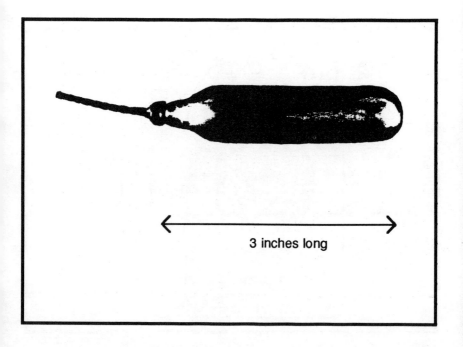

3 inches long

Explosive Cigarette Lighter

This device consists of a lighter from which most of the wadding has been removed and replaced with explosive filler. Part of the wadding is usually inserted at the bottom so that the lighter will appear to be normal. The wick has been removed and replaced with a fuse, and when the flint striker is activated, the fuse is ignited and the explosive is detonated. The only outward sign that this lighter has been altered is the added fuse.

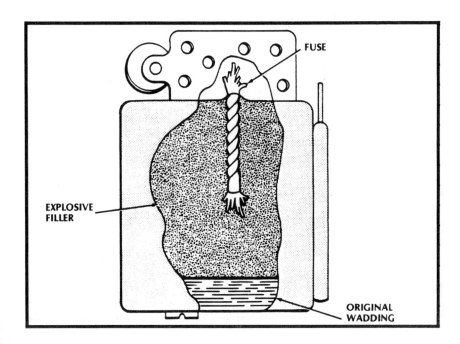

Explosive Fountain Pen

When the cap is unscrewed and removed from the pen barrel of this booby trap device, the two friction fuses ignite. This causes both the cap and the barrel to explode in the hands of the person holding the pen.

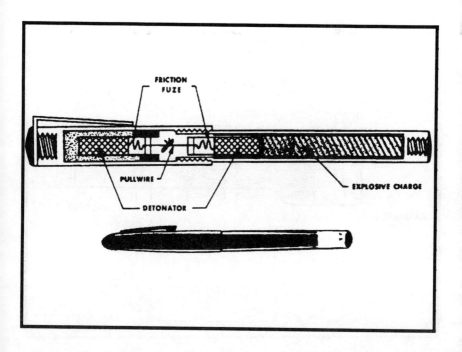

Flashlight Explosive

A standard flashlight, still using the normal contact switch and battery, is filled with black powder. The light bulb is broken, and the filament wires are exposed to the black powder mixture. Often a mirror or plastic lens covers the black powder and bulb so that a casual glance reveals nothing more than an ordinary flashlight. When the flashlight switch is pushed "on," the device detonates.

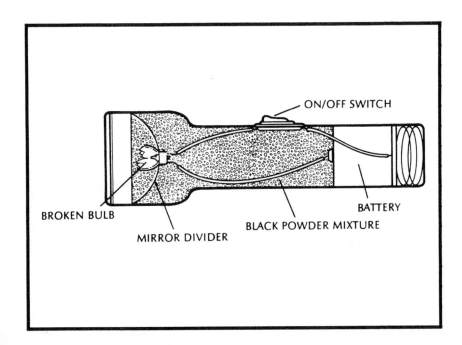

ON/OFF SWITCH

BROKEN BULB

MIRROR DIVIDER

BLACK POWDER MIXTURE

BATTERY

Gas Tank Bomb

A charge of plastic explosive is placed under a vehicle's gas tank, along with a battery and an electrical detonator. A plastic tube with a metal ball is meant to roll back and forth so that when a turn is made, the ball makes contact with the wires on one end of the tube and causes detonation. The device is usually held to the bottom of a vehicle with any combination of tape, wire, and glue.

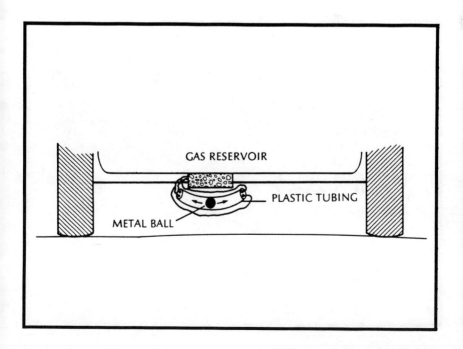

Impact Bomb

A weighted length of metal pipe, 6 inches or slightly longer, with a plunger device on one end that strikes a point of metal into a toy pistol cap made of black powder. The resulting ignition occurs as the bomb lands, fires the cap, and explodes the black powder packed in the pipe. The device can contain glass, tacks, BB's, etc. stuck to the pipe with glue to add to the fragmentation effect of the bomb.

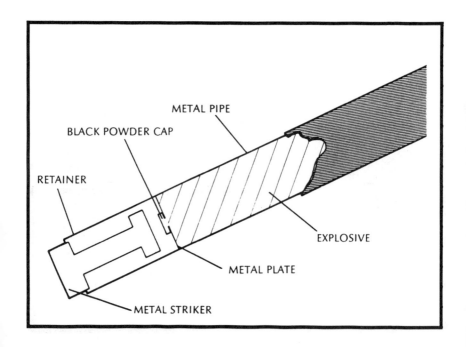

METAL PIPE

BLACK POWDER CAP

RETAINER

EXPLOSIVE

METAL PLATE

METAL STRIKER

Letter Bomb

There are numerous ways to trigger a letter bomb, and the device in this photo uses a photo electric switch. When the sealed envelope is opened, the photo-cell is subjected to light, thereby causing detonation. A simple music playing greeting card can easily be fashioned into an effective letter bomb.

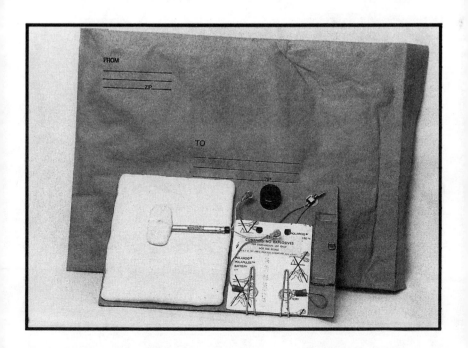

Mail Slot Incendiary

This type of device, first developed by the Irish Republican Army in 1930, is used to deliver an incendiary through a mail slot. Its consists of two plastic bags in a manilla envelope. One bag houses an acid sensitive mixture and a vial of acid encased in a rubber balloon or condom. The second bag is filled with gasoline to feed the fire. Prior to placing the device, the vial of acid is crushed, thereby allowing the acid to begin eating through the rubber until it makes contact with the acid sensitive mixture and ignites. Note: In this configuration, sometimes a thin passive membrane forms between the acid and the explosive mixture which prevents ignition. Any type of movement could also trigger instantaneous ignition of this device.

Mouse Trap Device

This bomb's explosive and firing system are housed in an ordinary first aid kit. This device uses a mousetrap switch which is activated when the lid of the box is opened by an unsuspecting person.

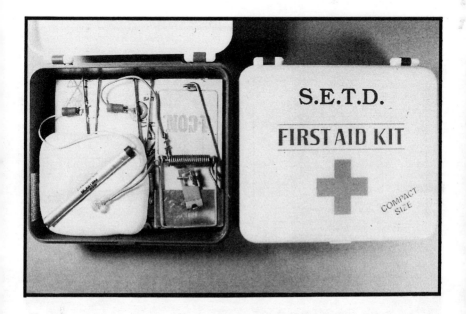

Package Bomb

The package bomb is similar to the letter bomb in its functioning, but the package bomb is capable of containing a larger quantity of explosives. The package bomb pictured here contains a one and one-quarter pound block of det-cord primed, C-4 plastic explosive which is activated by a wrist watch timer. Nails were added for a fragmentation effect.

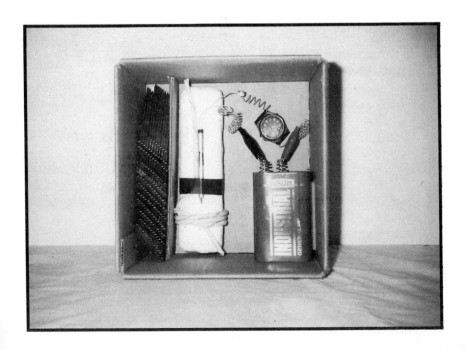

Pen Device

This improvised explosive device also helps to reinforce the fact that any item, no matter how small, can house explosives. This device is activated when the ball point pen's button is pushed down. Depending on the type of explosive filler used, this bomb is capable of maiming, or even killing a person.

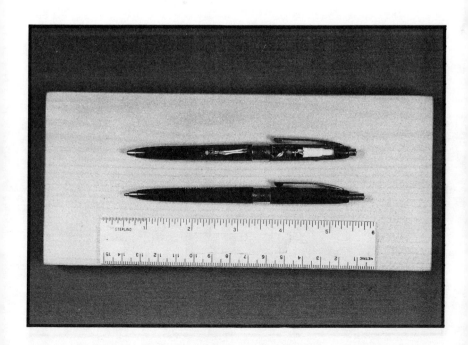

Pipe Bombs

Of all the explosive devices used, the pipe bomb is the most common. Although relatively simple in design, the pipe bomb is often constructed with various internal fusing mechanisms. These devices are usually designed to detonate in one of five basic ways: external fuse; photo electric switch; anti-handling (tilt) switch; time-delay switch; or the pressure release switch.

Pipe Bomb Impact Grenade

Also known as the "Torpedo Pipe Bomb," this device is capped with a plunger type detonator on each end. If the detonator is struck on either end, the force will make the plug and brass sleeve impact the .22 magnum cartridges, causing them to explode. It is believed that this type of device is popular among "outlaw type" motorcycle gangs.

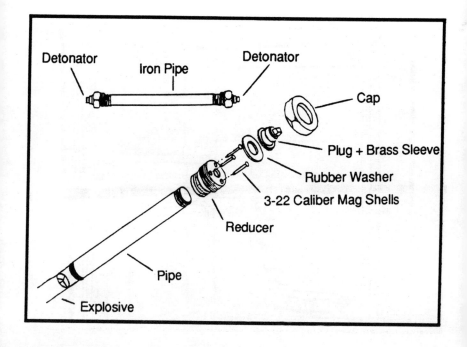

Refrigerator Bomb

Frequently used by drug dealers, the refrigerator bomb is intended to be set off by opening the refrigerator door. An electrical activated blasting cap detonates the explosive charge that can be made of plastic explosive, TNT, etc. The device is activated by having the wires from the blasting cap connected to the refrigerator's internal light socket. When the refrigerator is opened, the door switch supplies power to the light, which explodes the bomb. Unplugging the refrigerator from the electrical socket will prevent this type of explosion, but caution is advised since a bomb can be modified to explode whether the refrigerator is plugged in or not.

Shotgun Shell Bomb - One Shell

This device operates in a manner that is very similar to the "Shotgun Shell Bomb" constructed of multiple shells, although it looks different and does not have as devastating of an effect. Normally constructed with a 12 gauge 00 buck shotgun shell, it is designed to be thrown into the air. The large ball bearing provides added weight that enhances the possibility of proper impact, which detonates the primer as it strikes a hard surface. The buckshot usually travels across the ground, possibly striking the legs. Glued nails, BB's, etc., to the shotgun shell improves the fragmentation effect.

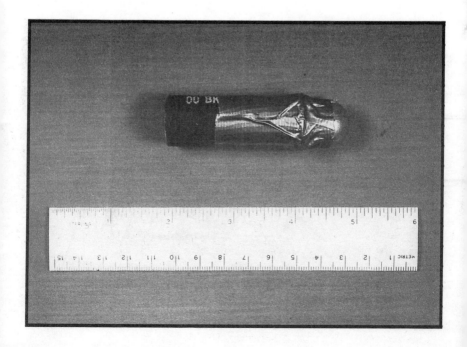

Shotgun Shell Bomb — Multiple Shells

This device is normally constructed of four ordinary shotgun shells with the area in between the shells filled with nails cemented in place with epoxy glue. The shells are wrapped firmly together with soft wire. BB's or small ball bearings are affixed with glue or tape over each shell's primer, which act as an impact source that fires each primer. Cardboard tail fins or cloth streamers stabilize the bombs to assure that they land on the primers. After detonation, this fragmentation bomb hurls parts of nails, wire, and other items in all directions.

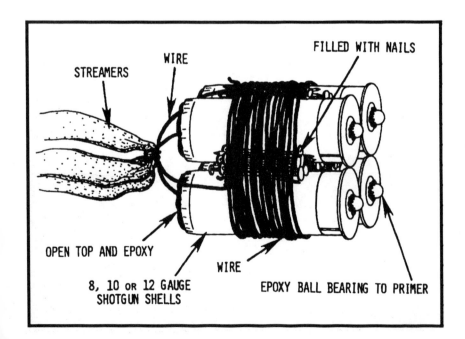

STREAMERS

WIRE

FILLED WITH NAILS

OPEN TOP AND EPOXY

8, 10 OR 12 GAUGE SHOTGUN SHELLS

WIRE

EPOXY BALL BEARING TO PRIMER

Shotgun Shell Bomb — Plunger Type

This device is very similar in effect to the "Shotgun Shell Bomb" with one shell, although it functions and looks somewhat different. This device has a steel bolt affixed through a washer that is taped onto the base of the shell. The bolt, which has a nut secured with glue and attached to the other side of the washer, can move freely through the washer. A BB or small ball bearing is glued to the top of the nut, which detonates the primer when the bolt strikes the ground. The fragmentation effect can be increased with the use of tacks, BB's, glass, etc.

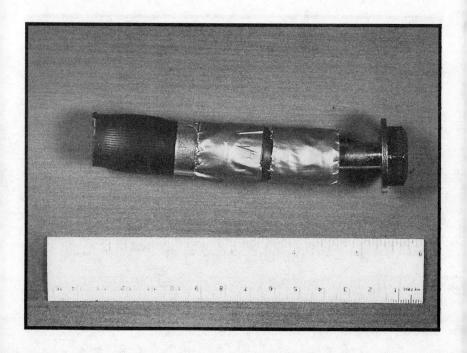

Spark Plug Explosive

This device, also known as the "Biker Explosive," is a lead pipe stuffed with black powder and buckshot or BB's. The device is ignited by the spark plug, which has one of the spark plug wires from a car, truck, or motorcycle attached to it. Depending on the explosive charge, it can maim or even kill.

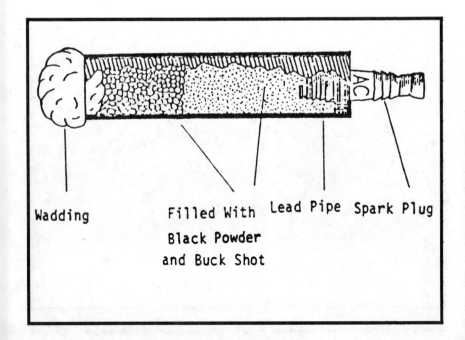

Wadding   Filled With   Lead Pipe Spark Plug
                 Black Powder
                 and Buck Shot

Tennis Ball Device

To many people the idea of an explosive device is likely to be 3 sticks of dynamite attached to a large ticking clock. The very concept that ordinary items could contain explosives is inconceivable. This tilt-activated explosive device is housed in three ordinary tennis balls, proving the point that explosive devices have no boundaries as to size or shape.

Section Five:

Miscellaneous Weapons

"The eye obeys exactly the action of the mind."

— Ralph Waldo Emerson

The miscellaneous weapons included in this section are the homemade, improvised, unconventional, disguised, unusual, and non-traditional weapons that do not fit into any other category or classification in the four previous sections of this book. Some of these weapons are rather crudely made, while others are of quality construction.

Chain Grip Come-A-Long

As a restraint, this device is used by holding on to both of the handles and placing a persons hand through the loop of the chain and twisting, placing pressure on the bones and nerves in the wrist. It may also be held by one handle and quickly spun over the wrist prior to twisting. Swinging and flailing actions allow this device to be used as a striking weapon also.

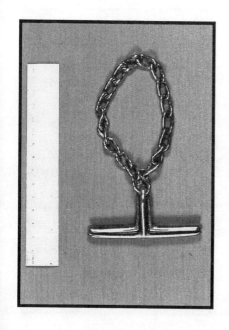
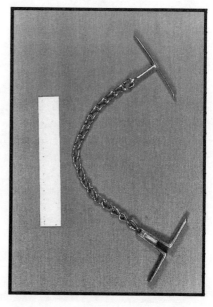

Cigarette Lighter Sprayer

This device looks like an ordinary "Bic" butane disposable cigarette lighter. It can be filled with virtually any "thin" liquid, including caustic or other dangerous substances, and sprays the liquid up to 10 feet.

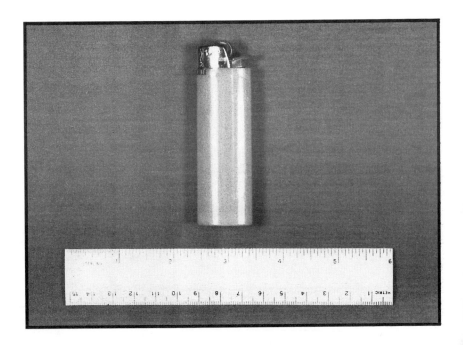

Cigarette Sprayer

When holding this device in the hand, it appears to be a normal lit cigarette. This "cigarette" will not, however, emit any smoke since the "lit" end is actually red and silver colored metal foil. A bulb is attached at the "unlit" end, and a tube runs through a small hole in the cigarette to the "lit" end. Virtually any "thin" liquid, including many irritants and inflammatories, can be contained in the bulb and sprayed into the eyes of a person at distances of up to 10 feet.

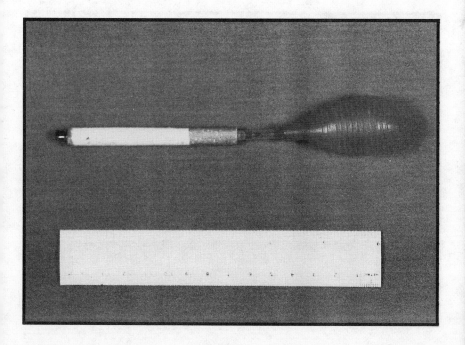

Electric Stun Guns

Most of these devices are designed to deliver 40,000 to 50,000 volts at low amperage and frequency. The device is supposed to interrupt voluntary muscle control on people receiving the electrical "zap" and render them harmless almost immediately when the two electrical contacts are held directly on them. A different version of the "Stun Gun," the "Taser" operates on the same principal, except it looks like a flashlight and fires two barbed prongs connected by electrical conducting wire up to a distance of 18 feet. Electrical current travels through the wires and barbs when the prongs penetrate the person's skin.

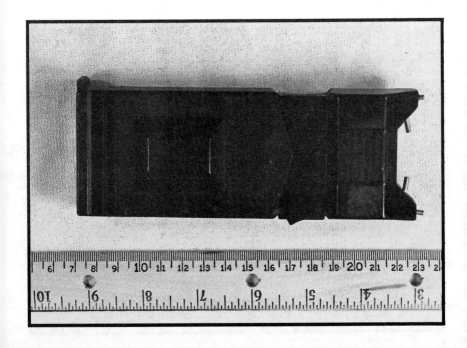

Fishing Hooks in Pant Seams

Standard black fishing hooks are carefully placed in the seams of a pair of blue or black denim pants, and is a popular ploy used by some "outlaw" type motorcycle gang members. The hooks face upward, and when someone frisks or grabs the person wearing them, the hooks pierce the fingers. The hooks have barbs on the end which makes the hooks difficult and painful to remove.

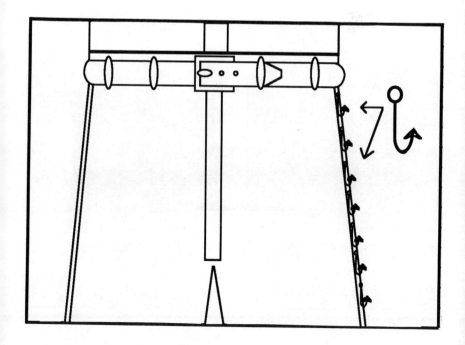

Iron Claw

This device is held in the hand by the ratchet with the "claw" open, looking somewhat like a modified handcuff. The "claw" is placed over the wrist and the ratchet turned for a tightening action on the wrist. Pressure on the wrist is released by sliding a collar up below the ratchet and turning the opposite way. The "Iron Claw" can be very painful and can break a human bone.

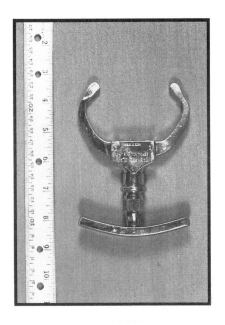 

Ju-Jo Magnum

When closed, this device made of high impact plastic, looks somewhat like a modified "Yawara" stick with a knuckle guard, and can be used in a manner similar to brass knuckles. One end unscrews, revealing a three-sided knife blade, which can then be turned around and screwed into the end for stabbing or slashing. The other end contains a nylon cord which can be pulled out for possible use as a garrote, for blocking, or to wrap around a body appendage as a control device.

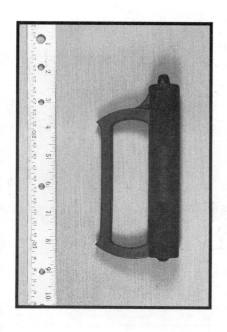
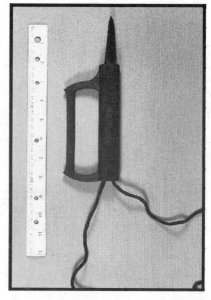

Penalyzer

Advertisements for this Israeli made device claim, "The pen is mightier than the sword." The "Penalyzer" looks like an executive-style pen, except that it is capable of giving up to 20 sprays of CS tear gas.

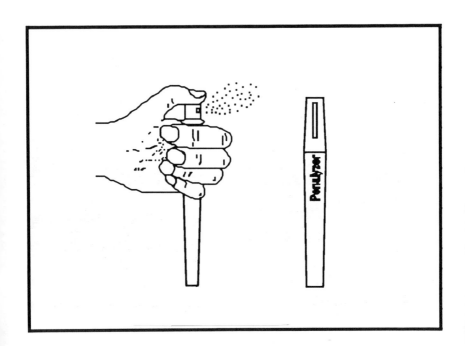

Pepsi Can Liquid Sprayer

This plastic "can" looks like an ordinary "Pepsi" can, until closely inspected. This can is actually a container for liquid with a battery operated pump which will spray virtually any light liquid from the front of the can. The pump is activated by pushing a button on the back of the can. This device can contain blinding acids, and irritating or inflammatory agents.

Slingshot

The picture here is a far cry from the child's play weapon made from the fork of a tree branch, rubber bands, and a swatch of leather. This model is capable of delivering fatal impact, particularly when used with marbles or steel ball bearings. This is not a toy — it is a dangerous weapon.

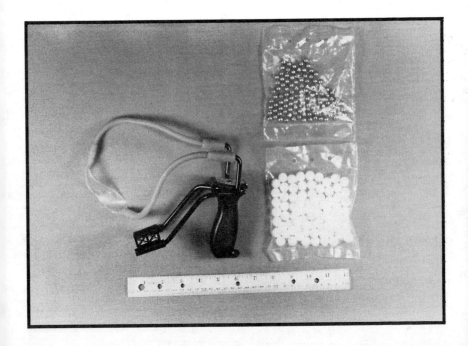

Watch-It

The size and shape of a man's wrist watch, this black plastic device contains pressurized CN tear gas. The "Watch-It" is aimed at a person's face and the spray button, located where a traditional watch stem is usually located, is depressed, releasing the spray up to 6 feet away.

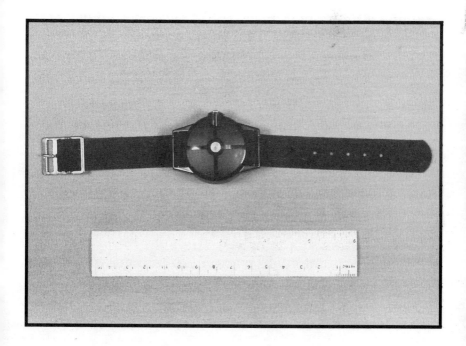

Section Six:

Concealed Carry Containers

"No object is mysterious. The mystery is your eye."

— Elizabeth Bowen

The containers in this section may be used to carry and conceal weapons, or virtually any other type of contraband (drugs, illegal items, etc.) that will fit into them. Some are quite large, such as an automobile battery, while others are as small as a coin. The containers listed in this section are not the only types available. There are many more commercially available containers and an unlimited amount of homemade ones. The only thing limiting the types of homemade containers is ingenuity.

Book Safe

The "Book Safe," pictured here, contains an "AMT .380 Backup," and is commercially manufactured. It can also be easily homemade by using a razor blade to cut the book's pages and to create a middle compartment. When on a shelf, in the hand, or in a briefcase, the "Book Safe" is almost impossible to detect.

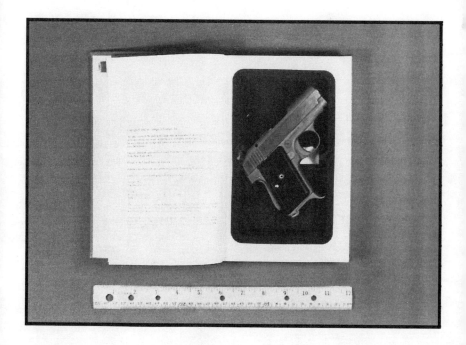

Car Battery Safe

This large and heavy 12 volt "Car Battery Safe" looks and feels like a real battery. The top lifts off completely and provides a deep area that can even conceal a large framed semi-auto pistol. Drug dealers frequently use this device by placing grease on the battery posts to add realism. They may also carry it in their car trunk with a note on top, "Will not take a charge."

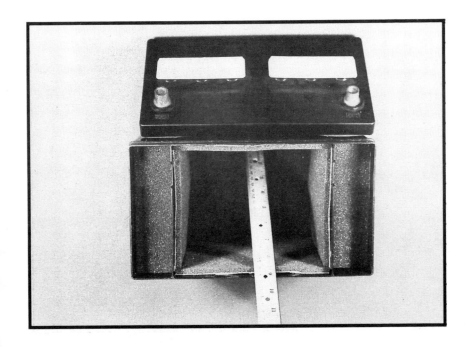

Coin and Pager Containers

The Eisenhower Dollar pictured below is commercially made and virtually impossible to tell from a real coin. It can only be opened by applying pressure to a certain spot on the coin   The pager is a standard pager with the battery removed. These devices are usually used to carry drugs, but can also contain blinding or irritating substances.

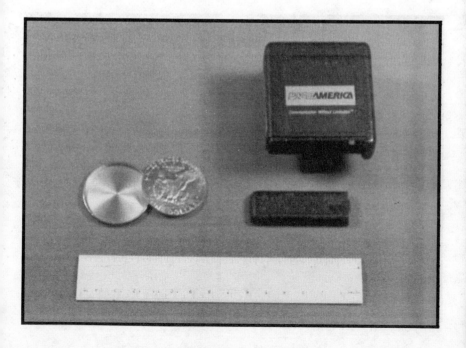

Keychain Box

A small box on the end of a keychain that is normally used to carry a small address and phone book. The book has been removed and the box, pictured here, contains a single edged razor blade. The box could also be used to carry drugs or caustic substances.

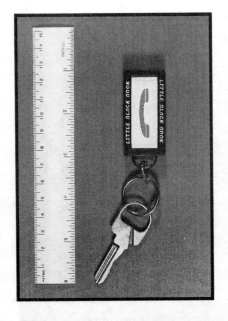 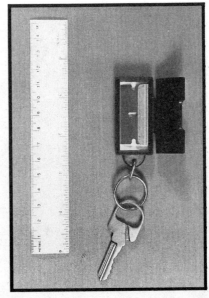

Magazine or Newspaper Carry Method

Almost any magazine or newspaper can be used to carry and conceal many different weapons effectively. The magazine pictured here conceals a device used for stabbing when held in the hand, or as a throwing knife. A sawed off shotgun can even be concealed in a rolled-up newspaper. Since both magazines and newspapers are flat, they are not normally thought of as effective concealed carry containers, and may be overlooked as such.

Product Safes

These items have the look, weight, and feel of the actual products. The items pictured open from either the top, or the bottom, and are not actually used for the products labeled. An Aqua Net hair spray container comes empty, but features a special stem for filling the item with almost any spray. These items easily conceal many types of weapons or drugs, and they are extremely difficult to distinguish from the real thing. Genuine empty product containers, such as Ajax and Planter's Cheese Balls, can also be used to conceal items.

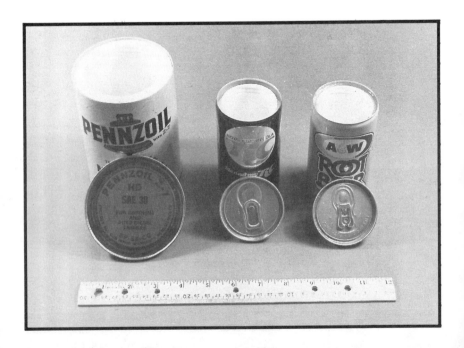

Section Seven:

Of Special Interest to Law Enforcement

"The wise man avoids evil by anticipating it."

— Publilius Syrus

The purpose of this section is two fold. First, there are numerous escape devices included that officers should be aware of since in custody subjects may try to escape or harm officers and others. Second, a number of items that may be of particular interest to law enforcement officers are included. Many of these can be used effectively by plainclothes or off-duty officers who want to remain covert, yet armed. Police officers should remember that many of the weapons and devices listed in the previous sections of this book can be used legitimately by on-duty and off-duty police officers. The bottom line is simple: Any item that can be carried by police officers or legitimate citizens can also be carried by the "bad guys." There is no substitute for caution.

Assorted Handcuff Keys

There is an assortment of handcuff keys available. Some of them can be fashioned from hair pins or paper clips, while others can be attached to the ends of writing pens, make-up applicators, or carried in tiny compartments.

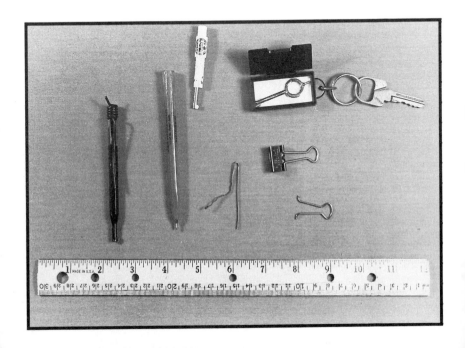

Ball Point Pen Refill Handcuff Key

A standard metal ball point refill is modified by cutting a small notch on the end of the non-ball point end and flaring the notched metal out so that it resembles the end of a standard handcuff key. This type of key works remarkably well and can even be carried as a functioning refill inside a standard ball point pen.

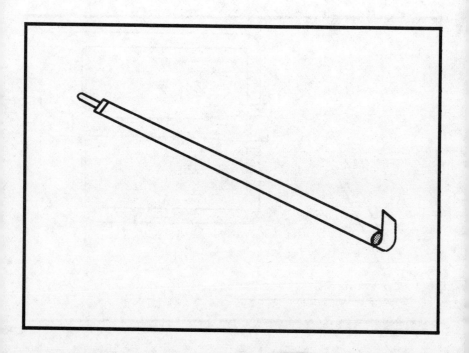

Belt Buckle Back-Up

The tongue of this belt buckle has been specially shaped as a fully functional standard handcuff key. The belt buckle, which may also be known as the "Brannigan Back-Up," was designed for police officers as a "back-up" handcuff key, should they ever be disarmed and handcuffed.

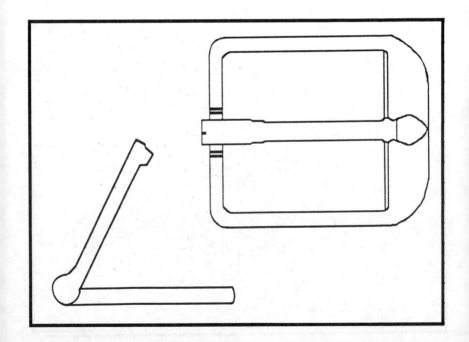

Cross Handcuff /Leg Iron Key

This homemade device is fashioned from two standard handcuff keys and one leg iron key. When worn around the neck on a chain as a necklace, this escape device may be difficult to spot and identify.

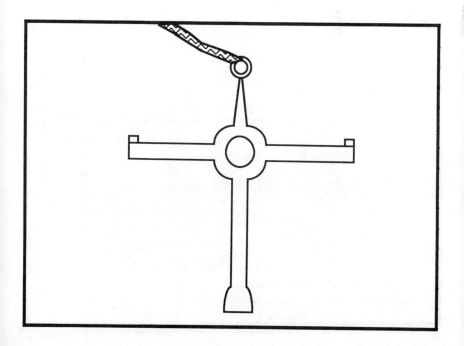

Guardian Attache

This all leather constructed attache has a velcro closure hidden compartment that is able to house virtually any large framed handgun. It also serves as a fully functioning attache. The special design of this case allows quick access to a handgun.

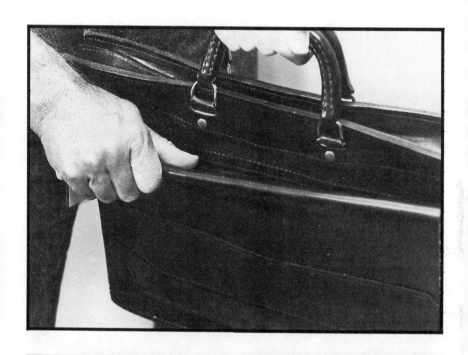

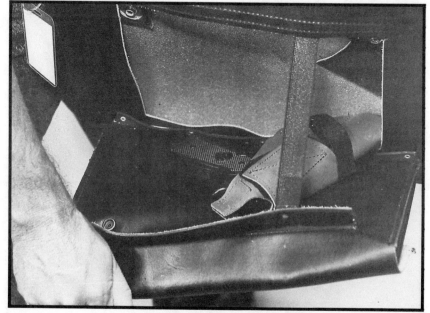

Guardian Equipment Bag

Constructed of ballistic nylon, this bag can be used to carry equipment, as a gym bag, as an overnight bag, or even as a large soft attache. It features a velcro closure hidden middle compartment with a hidden holster that can conceal even a large framed revolver or semi-auto pistol.

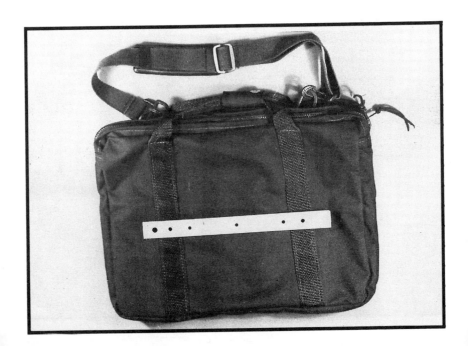

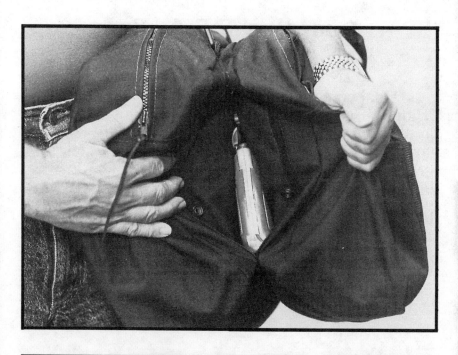

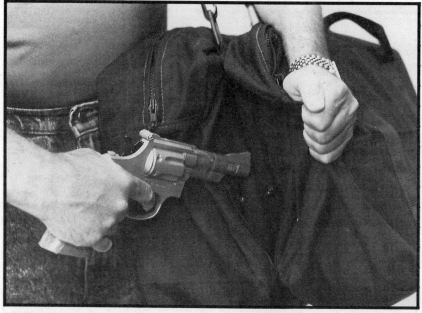

Guardian U.S.A. Bag

This personal bag, similar in concept to the "Hidden Agenda Bag," although this one is carried in the hand, can contain most duty gear for the civilian dressed or off-duty police officer. It features a unique removable hand strap that is best used by wearing the strap over the wrist and securing the other end to the butt of a handgun. The handgun is concealed in a velcro closed compartment, and can be quickly deployed simply by pulling the strap away from the bag, which leaves the handgun secured to the strap in the hand. Made of quality leather.

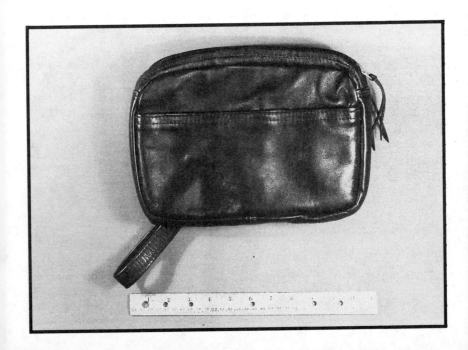

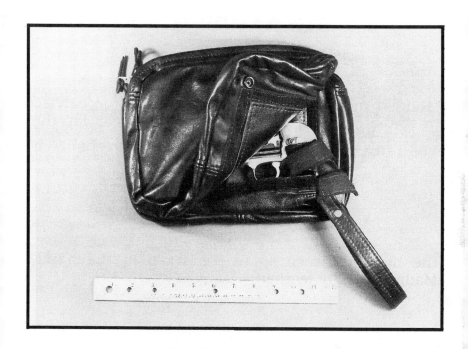

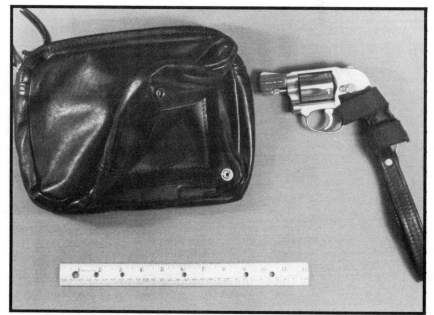

Gunny Sack

This bag does not feature the hidden "POLICE" ID flap system, or allow access to the handgun as quickly as the "Hidden Agenda Bag." It is somewhat smaller and constructed of durable ballistic nylon.

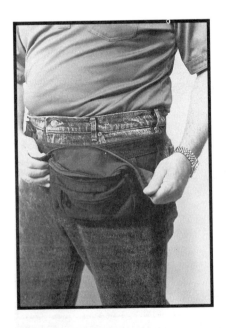 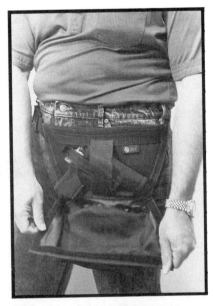

Handcuff Key Hidden on Belt Buckle

A standard handcuff key can be effectively hidden as a back-up by police officers when the round top of the key is held with a snap closure on the back of almost any removable belt buckle. Another method of carrying a back-up handcuff key on the belt is to simply tape the key to the inside of the belt, preferably on the back since the handcuffs may also be placed behind the back. Some officers tape a key to both the front and back of the belt, just in case they are handcuffed in either manner.

Handcuff Key Keychain

The most common type of handcuff key key-chain is a miniature version of the PR-24® Police Baton. These keychains are manufactured in black and chrome, and function well as a handcuff key. They are very popular with working police officers.

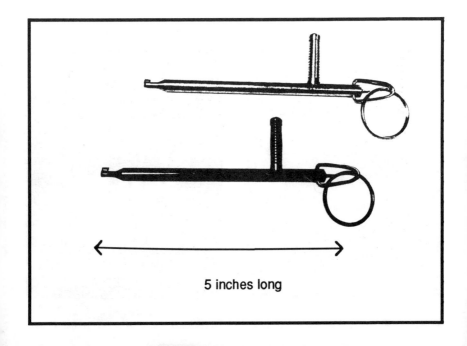

5 inches long

Hidden Agenda Bag

Constructed of ballistic nylon, this bag can contain a great deal of police duty gear for the plain clothes or off-duty police officer. A built-in holster on a velcro closure allows quick access to the handgun, while the middle compartment can hold extra ammo or magazines, handcuffs, expandable baton, mini-flashlight, and other gear. The outside cloth flap can be quickly pulled from the hidden outer pocket and features a special flap with "POLICE" printed on it in a reflective material. This bag is ideal for hot weather use since concealability may be a problem.

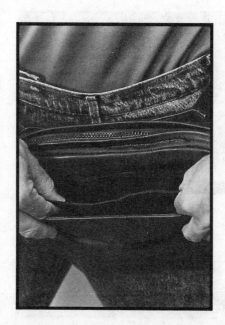

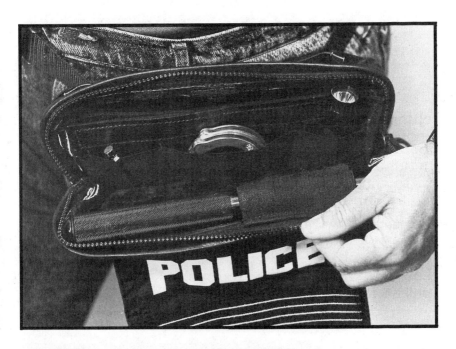

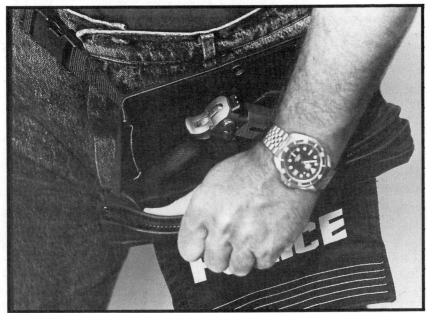

Afterword

The authors actively seek comments, suggestions, and contributions from the readers of this book. Please provide us with information relating to any "Street Weapons." This includes weapons in this book and other types of "Street Weapons" which were not included. Please send us any of the following:

— If possible, actual "Street Weapons" not included in this book. They will be returned upon request.

— If the weapons are unavailable, please send clear black and white photos or line drawings along with a written description of the weapons.

— Where to purchase and costs of new, commercially produced "Street Weapons."

— Complete police reports or other incident reports on any "Street Weapons," including those listed in this books. If reports are unavailable, please include the following:

1. The type of weapon seized and where this weapon was carried.
2. The sex, age, height, weight, criminal record, sobriety, and other pertinent data of the person possessing the weapon.
3. If the weapon was used, how was it used, and what type of injury was sustained.
4. Any assault against a law enforcement officer. The date, time, location, and any other data relevant to the incident.

— How any homemade "Street Weapons," not included in this book, are made, including the necessary material and construction design for building the weapon. Photos and line drawings would be helpful.

Your active contributions and our collection of meaningful data and weapons will ultimately be available, and undoubtedly, assist in further informing our nation's police officers. Please take a little time to share and care by sending this information to:

Edward J. Nowicki and Dennis A. Ramsey
c/o Performance Dimensions Publishing
P.O. Box 502
Powers Lake, WI 53159-0502
Phone (414)279-3850.

Bibliography

Nowicki, Edward J. "The Cutting Edge," *Police*, Vol.13, No. 4, 1989, pp. 37-40, p. 48.

Nowicki, Edward J. "Onion Field Insurance," *Police*, Vol. 14, No. 7, 1990, pp. 24-28.

Nowicki, Edward J. "Caution Versus Paranoia," *The Police Marksman*, Vol. XII, No. 2, 1987, pp. 38-39.

Nowicki, Edward J. "The Role of Training," *Police*, Vol. 11, No. 9, 1987, pp. 25-26, pp. 38-39.

Nowicki, Edward J. "Taking Off the Kid Gloves," *Police*, Vol. 14, No. 7, 1990, pp. 53-55, 84-86.

Nowicki, Edward J. "The Power of Fear," *Combat Handguns*, Vol. 9, No. 3, 1988, p. 74.

Rossi, Guy A. "Out of Sight — Out of Mind," *Police*, Vol. 14, No. 5, 1990, pp. 38-43.

Remsberg, Charles, *The Tactical Edge*, Northbrook, IL: Calibre Press, 1986.

Department of Justice, U.S. Marshals Service, *Improvised Weapons and Escape Devices*, Glynco, GA: FLETC, undated.

California Department of Justice, *Disguised Weapons Handbook*, Sacramento, CA: Bureau of Organized Crime and Criminal Intelligence, 1983.

Nowicki, Edward J. "Mini Guns — Useful or Useless?" *Combat Handguns*, Vol. 1, No. 1, 1989, pp. 20-23, p. 67.

Nowicki, Edward J. "Pocket Shooting," *Pocket Pistol Handbook*, Vol. 1, No. 1, 1989, pp. 4-7.

Nowicki, Edward J. "The Professional's Hideaway," *Pocket Pistol Handbook*, Vol. 2, No. 2, 1990, pp. 48-53.

Nowicki, Edward J. "Concealed Carry: When It's Too Hot!" *Guns and Weapons for Law Enforcement*, Vol. 2, No. 1, 1990, pp. 16-18, pp. 78-80.

Nowicki, Edward J. "Cold Weather Carry Options," *Guns and Weapons for Law Enforcement*, Vol. 3, No. 1, 1991, pp. 16-19.

Nowicki, Edward J. "Survival Undercover," *Police*, Vol. 11, No. 5, 1987, p. 22, pp. 24-28.

Department of the Treasury, *Disguised Weapons*, Washington, DC: U.S. Customs Service, 1979.

Dallas Police Department, *Disguised Weapons Manual*, Dallas, TX: Dallas Police Department Safety Unit, 1987.

Appel, Ronald and Rolfe, *Disguised and Concealed Weapons Handbook 1990-91*, Sacramento, CA: California Department of Justice, 1990.

Biography

Edward J. Nowicki is one of the nation's leading law enforcement trainers in addition to being the Executive Director of the nation's largest law enforcement training association, the prestigious Am. Society of Law Enforcement Trainers, ASLET. A continuous sworn police officer since 1968, Ed currently works part-time as a police officer for the Twin Lakes, Wisconsin Police Department. A survivor of six separate shooting incidents, he began his law enforcement career with the Chicago Police Department and has held the ranks of Patrolman, Detective, Lieutenant, and Chief of Police with four law enforcement agencies. Since 1981, Ed has been employed full-time as a Police Training Specialist with Milwaukee Area Technical College. He has trained thousands of police officers across the nation, in addition to conducting training in Europe for the U.S. Military on numerous occasions.

Edward J. Nowicki has been judicially recognized and declared an expert on police training, and has received many awards for his work and contributions to law enforcement and law enforcement training. A widely published author for various law enforcement publications and a former Municipal Judge, he holds a Bachelor of Science Degree in Criminal Justice and a Master of Arts Degree in Management.

Biography

Dennis A. Ramsey, or **"Ramsey"** as he is known to his friends and colleagues, began his career in law enforcement in 1968 and has trained thousands of police and security personnel across the nation. Since 1985, Ramsey has been employed full-time as an Enforcement Supervisor over state-wide investigations conducted by the State of Illinois, Dept. of Professional Regulation. He has served as the Illinois State Director for the American Society of Law Enforcement Trainers (ASLET) since it was formed in 1987. His attendance at numerous training programs have earned him several awards, certificates, and titles ranging from instructor, to international instructor.

As a result of **Dennis A. Ramsey** traveling around the nation conducting "Street Weapon" seminars for such organizations as the Law Enforcement Television Network (LETN), L.E. Net, and various colleges and law enforcement agencies, he has earned national recognition as an expert on "Street Weapons." Due to his never ending thirst for knowledge, Ramsey is currently earning his Bachelor's Degree from Northeastern Illinois University.

*"To see things as they are, the eyes must be open;
to see things as other than they are, they must be
open even wider; to see things as better than
they are, they must be open to the full."*

— Antonio Machado

Order Form

Telephone Orders: Call (414)279-3850. Have your Mastercard or Visa ready.

Postal Orders: Performance Dimensions Publishing, P.O. Box 502, Powers Lake, WI 53159-0502, U.S.A., (414)279-3850.

Please send the following:

Quantity	Title	Price Each	Total
	Street Weapons (the book)	$19.95	
	Street Weapons: The Video	$29.95	
	Sales Tax: Wisconsin Residents add 6%		
	Shipping & Handling	$ 3.00	
	Total Enclosed		$

☐ Please send FREE information about other books and videos when published.

☐ I would like to host a *Street Weapons* Seminar.

Method of Payment:

☐ Check   ☐ Money Order   ☐ Mastercard   ☐ Visa

If credit card: Card Number

_____

Name on Credit Card

_____

Signature _____ Expires _____

Send to my: ☐ Work   ☐ Home

Name_____ Title _____

Agency/Company _____

Address _____

City _____ State _____ Zip _____

Agency/Company Phone ( )_____

Home Phone ( )_____

WHY WAIT? Call your order in to us RIGHT NOW!